The Word Wasp
Hornet
Literacy Primer

Phonics & Structure
A Manual for Teaching the Basic Rules and Structures of English
(Reading and Spelling)

Harry Cowling & Marie Cowling

Published in the year 2005 by H. J. Cowling & M. Cowling, Pudsey, West Yorkshire

First Edition	February	2005	ISBN 0-9538714-2-8
Revised Edition	December	2008	
Second Revised Edition	October	2010	
Third Revised Edition	September	2013	
Fourth Revised Edition	September	2015	

Photocopying

People cite any number of reasons for poor literacy skills. They are a matter of complete indifference to the individual with the problem. For these people, the problem is deeply personal. The Hornet Literacy Primer is for the individual student. It is an unassuming text which teaches literacy skills without recourse to patronising gimmicks and childish graphics. It is for those students who aspire to sit alongside their literate peers and share the same opportunities without drawing undue attention to their struggle. The Hornet Literacy Primer is their record of achievement. Some students will learn faster than others therefore it is a necessary requirement that each individual has their own book.

Experience has also revealed that many teachers take it upon themselves to form ad hoc programmes; using parts of one programme in the hope that it will complement another. The Hornet Literacy Primer stands on its own and its effects will be diminished and not strengthened by photocopying.

Photocopying will not be permitted under any circumstances.

Acknowledgements

We would like to thank:

Val Miller (UWCN) for her kindness and for overturning the stone under which Harry had been hiding since the publication of Toe by Toe.

Phil Jackson (SENCO), and the learning support assistants, at Crawshaw School Pudsey, who supported our trials.

We would like to give particular thanks to Elaine Watts for her support, commitment and hard work.

There are many people, students and coaches, whose names belong on this page: far too many to list! However, one person, the first student of both Toe by Toe and The Word Wasp, to whom the highest praise should be given, now the best literacy coach that I know: my wife Marie has been an invaluable asset. Without her patience, sympathy, common sense and understanding; this text would still be on the drawing board.

HJC & MC

5

Who will Benefit from the Hornet?

Primary Schools

Many primary schools are reluctant to buy texts which their students might not complete before progressing to high school. The Hornet allows for earlier intervention at a more basic level and at a much lower price.

All Students from the Age of Six

The Hornet is a literacy primer and it has been designed as a programme to give basic literacy skills to anyone who needs to learn them. It is the ideal 'kick start' to literacy and can be used by concerned parents to support their children. All children need to learn the rules of English and their progress through school can be made easier by following the exercises within this text.

Children and Adults with Severe Literacy Problems

It is particularly useful with children who have been diagnosed as having special educational needs; including students who have been described as dyslexic. **It was developed with 'statemented' students whose literacy problems could only be described as 'severe'.**

Like its companion text (The Word Wasp) the Hornet was developed with both dyslexic adults and children. It is, therefore, free from any kind of language or graphics which could be deemed as patronising.

Why do we need Phonics?

Professor Diane McGuinness, in a fascinating article: No. 49 - A Prototype for Teaching the English Alphabet Code: published on behalf of the Reading Reform Society, makes the point that the scientific research of the development of language over a 5000 year period shows not a jot of evidence that any language was based on a whole word system. The tenets of that article should be tattooed on the foreheads of those unwise and unwilling mandarins whose policies have lead to the growing misery of illiteracy.

> The deciphering of the Rosetta Stone was finally achieved when eminent scholars abandoned the idea that hieroglyphs represented a pictorial language and found the phonic translations of an early Greek script within the hieroglyphs.

In spite of the historical evidence, and that which the ancients wouldn't even need to consider as common sense, a whole Special Needs empire was built on the premiss that literacy was about memory and therefore the problem, according to them, lay within the structures of a student's brain. The whole word systems, which dominated the Special Needs approach to literacy, were drip fed into our education system since the late 1920s until the post Plowden/ Warnock era when they were poured in!

Students who failed to learn by whole word systems were then fed a diet of multi-sensory banalities which served to alienate rather than educate.

Schools could deliver subject based education but they could not be relied upon to deliver the tools to learn the subjects. Governments swept the issue under the carpet or threw money at the problem but no-one delivered the goods. Literacy is a political issue and has been throughout history.

Unfortunately, schools are not always able to maintain literacy programmes for a number of reasons. By the time a literacy problem has been diagnosed it is often too late to address and when a problem is discovered students are often given palliatives in the form of word recognition and multi-sensory teaching programmes. These programmes do not address the problem. They only serve to destroy a student's confidence. Literacy is not about remembering the letter order of frequently used words. Our language is based on a phonetic code. Fail to teach the code: fail to teach the language! Thankfully, particularly in primary schools, phonics is back on the national agenda.

The school system relies on the educational development of all students to take place simultaneously. Nature declares otherwise! An enlightening comparison can be made between education and horticulture: If we throw grass seeds on a patch of prepared soil we might find that after a few days some seeds have germinated. Several days later more seeds may have germinated but we recognize the folly of only fertilizing those seeds which germinated first.

The logic is easy to follow so why do we presume that students who cannot grasp the abstract concepts of literacy, immediately after their introduction to them, should have to spend the rest of their lives at a disadvantage to those who did learn them?

If a child falters at the elementary level then they will find themselves falling behind others until a point is reached where education gives way to alienation. Ask any adult dyslexic! The main benefit of developing a special needs programme with adults is the access to objective feedback. The success of the Hornet and the Word Wasp is due to the unabashed heart-pourings of adults who can remember, only too well, the process of falling behind.

The Hornet is a tool designed to make level the academic playing fields and to allow all students access to our language by allowing those with literacy skills, from any walk of life, to teach those without.

Any literate person can use the Hornet or the Word Wasp. Parents should not be responsible for the development of their children's literacy skills but the problem is too serious to allow this neglect to go unchecked. **Teachers are often under great pressure and the help of parents or volunteers is much appreciated.**

The Word Wasp is used in schools, both in the U.K. and overseas, to teach literacy, from the Orkneys to the Isle of Wight, from Japan to Bosnia. It is used in both prisons and young offender units. The Hornet will share the same distribution, and like the Word Wasp, it was designed on the kitchen table; for the kitchen table.

Students should have the ability to make informed choices about their own lives. Through literacy we can achieve that goal and then we can start to build an informed society.

The Development of the Hornet

The trial of The Word Wasp at a school in West Yorkshire has been a resounding success. Most Wasp students have had their reading and spelling skills advanced to levels that some commentators have described as incredible. However, there were other students whose problems were considered insurmountable.

Those students had no discernible reading or spelling age. Speech too, was seriously impaired and fine motor skills had not been developed which meant that handwriting was another major obstacle.

Those students were in danger of being 'written off' because the resources available did absolutely nothing to initiate or stimulate any process of sequential thinking. Those twelve-year old students were unable to remember their own birth dates or their home telephone numbers. They were unaware of concepts of time or distance. They presented the Wasp coaching team with their most serious challenge.

It soon became obvious that the Wasp was making a difference but it was also obvious that the programme was too fast for severely challenged students.

It was also noticed that a system to develop auditory discrimination was needed. In order to facilitate such problems, the Hornet includes exercises which stimulate a student's ability to discriminate between vowel sounds. The exercises have been reduced to smaller, and slower steps.

The progress being made by Hornet students is remarkable. They now have discernible reading and spelling ages but, above all, they feel a sense of inclusion and they are developing thinking skills!

Welcome to The New Edition

Thanks to the increasing use of both the Hornet and the Word Wasp our feedback base has increased significantly and allowed us to integrate the constructive findings of parents, teachers and students, with our own research to produce a sharper, shorter and more efficient programme.

The format is much the same but the colour coding plays a much more useful role and makes for the easier translation of instructions. It also serves to demonstrate how wonderfully simple are the rules of our language.

We have also introduced 'x' and the sound of the letter 'y'. Unstressed letters have always been a source of frustration and we have taken steps to minimise their impact on the learning process.

The print is much larger and we have undertaken some serious but prudent textual surgery with regard to the length of the exercises. As a result, the text is much faster and easier to use.

Harry and Marie Cowling

September 2015

Basic Instructions

You will need:
A student
The Hornet
A lined exercise book
Scrap paper
A pencil
A pen
A table
Patience

If your student is right-handed you must sit to his/her left in order that you can see the spellings as they are being written. Reverse the positions for left-handed students.

Corners are best but it is not an absolute necessity!

Wherever possible, you must try to see a word as it is being written. This is not always easy with left-handed students.

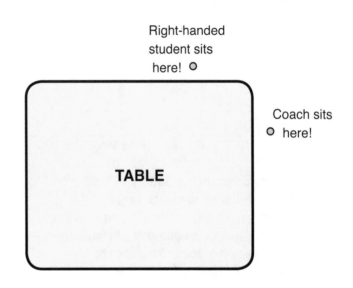

Right-handed
student sits
here! ⊙

Coach sits
⊙ here!

TABLE

Instructions: Marking the Exercises

Look for two consecutive ticks (two together)

Day	8	9	11	15	16	
Month	4	4	4	4	4	
Spell						
aft	/	·	/	·	/	unfinished
eft	/	·	/	/		completed
art	·	·	/	·	/	unfinished
oft	/	/				completed
gift	·	/	/			completed

The example **above** shows the pattern of ticks required before a student's spelling can be considered consistent enough to leave and move on. An exercise column has been completed when each word has two consecutive ticks. **The same instructions apply to the reading columns.**

An exercise session begins by placing the date in the first column of the exercise grid. The example on the page **opposite** shows that the initial exercise began on August 2nd; continued on August 4th and then the 7th and 8th respectively. Place the date at the top of the column before you begin.

Work down each dated column, ticking or dotting each word or sound as required: a tick for a correct answer, a dot for an incorrect answer.

Spelling or Pro (reading): The words in the white **Pro** (reading) columns are for your student to read out loud; pronouncing each one in his/her normal manner of speech.

The words in the blue **Spell** (spelling) columns are for the coach to read to his/her student. The student must then repeat the word or sound, to ensure that they have heard the coach correctly, before writing the spelling. The blue background and italic print have been used to prevent the student's easy visual access to the spellings.

How long should a lesson be?

Between 20 and 40 minutes a session is usually enough! It isn't necessary to use the book on a daily basis but the more often you work with a student, the faster her/his progress will be. Much depends on your student's writing ability. Lined paper is preferable.

Day	2	4	7	8			Day	2	4	7	8	9		Day	2	4	7				Day	2	4	7	8		
Month	8	8	8	8			Month	8	8	8	8	8		Month	8	8	8				Month	8	8	8	8		
Pro							Spell							Spell							Spell						
scr	/	·	/	/			spot	/	/					brat	/	/					croft	/	/				
shr	/	/					skin	/	/					thrift	·	/	/				smug	/	/				
squ	/	/					brag	/	/					smog	/	/					twist	/					
squid	/	/					brim							blend	/	/					twill	/					
spr	·	·	/	/			bliss	/	/					strap	/	/					bless						
str	/	/					dross	/	/					splash	·	/	/				flesh	/	/				
spr	/	/					cram	/	/					grip	/	/					flash	/	·	/	/		
sprig	/	/					fret	/	/					strip	/	/					struck	/	/				
thrip	/	/					slush	·	/	·	/	/		glass	/	/					shred	/	/				
split	/	/					throb	/	/					thrash	/	/					split	/	/				

Do not attempt the same column twice in the same day: one attempt for one tick or dot!
Never allow a student to start a column that he/she will be unable to finish before the end of the lesson. The coach needs the book, some scrap paper and a pen; the student needs a pencil and a lined exercise book.

Preparation
Speaking for Spelling

A student with literacy problems has to rely on the vagaries of received sound. When a coach is reading words for spelling, it is vital that a student hears every syllable clearly before attempting to spell a particular sound or word.

Strategy:

The coach must look directly at the student as he/she reads the word or sound to be spelled.

The student must be looking directly at the mouth of the coach.

The student must acknowledge that they have heard the sound or word by repeating it.

If the coach is satisfied that the student has heard the word or sound correctly then the student may write the word or sound.

Students should be encouraged to spell out-loud the sounds as they are being written. Remember! Sounds: '**a**' as in '**a**nt', '**b**' as in '**b**ag'.

Coaches who follow this process will be aware of any weaknesses immediately and will thus be able to correct and guide the student. It is vital that the process of spelling and writing the sounds becomes simultaneous.

It will not take long for this process to become automatic.

Be aware of students who appear reluctant. Check that members of his or her peer group are not in the vicinity. It is vital that your student is familiar with the basic sounds of our language. **It is not necessary to sacrifice a student's dignity in the process.**

Colour Coding Instructions

Green letters = Vowel sounds: cat hem pig dog hut

Red letters = Vowel names: pave theme spike

Blue letters = Silent: which switch what

Amber letters = Warnings: any many do not make the correct vowel sound.

Amber letters = Warnings: was wash want. 'a' after 'w' makes the sound 'o'.

Amber letters = Unstressed vowels Instructions are on **Page 76**

Amber letters = Unstressed letters (er) butter winter **Page 152**

Black Bold words
Words in **bold black print** are not phonetically decodable and can be revealed to students and still earn a tick.

Coach

Sounds are vital!

The letter **sounds** of the alphabet can be divided into consonants and vowels. These **sounds** are put together to form words.

Letters also have **names.** The **names** and the **sounds** of the **vowels** and the **sounds** of the **consonants** are used in the formation of words: **We never use the names of the consonants!**

The grid on the opposite page shows the sounds made by the letters of our alphabet.
The vowel sounds have been highlighted in green print. The difference between vowel sounds and vowel names is necessary for a proper understanding of our language.

The sounds are: 'a' as in 'ant', 'b' as in 'bag', 'd' as in 'dog' etc. The vowel names (printed in red) are 'a' as in 'ape', 'e' as in 'ego', 'i' as in 'idea', 'o' as in 'open', 'u' as in 'unit'. **We will deal with these later.**

Strategy:

Point to each square and ask your student for the **letter** sound **alone**; not the whole word! The coach can assist the student by reading the word if necessary.

Work down or up the squares. Avoid working horizontally. Students know that 'a' is followed by 'b'. Guessing must be discouraged.

When a student encounters a green letter (a vowel sound) they must indicate that the letter is a vowel by saying: "a **vowel** - e **vowel**" etc. Upper case vowels (capitals) are not entitled to say their name anymore than lower case vowels!

Don't forget:

This exercise is dealing with sounds; not names. The sounds are 'a' as in 'ant', 'b' as in 'bag' etc.

'ay' 'bee' 'see' 'dee' are out !!!!!!

a A ant	b B bag	c C cat	d D dog	e E egg	f F fog
g G gum	h H hat	i I ink	j J jam	k K kiss	l L lemon
m M mud	n N nail	o O orange	p P pet	qu Qu quid	r R rat
s S sock	t T top	u U up	v V vet	w W wasp	y Y yes
z Z zebra	ch chip	sh ship	th then	th thin	ck lock

Please note: The letter 'x' is not represented here. It is introduced on page 54.

Coach

Letter Sounds

This exercise introduces the basic sounds which form the building blocks of the English language. A thorough understanding of these sounds is crucial before we can progress through the exercises.

The sounds of the letters are distinctly different to the names of the letters.

The sounds are :

'a' (**as in a**nt)
'b' (**as in b**ag)
'c' (**as in c**at)

If you are unsure of the sounds you may consult the grid on the previous page.

Important information

The letter '**s**' has two sounds: Say the word 'ye**s**' and listen to the sound of the letter '**s**'. Then listen to the sound of the letter '**s**' in the word 'hi**s**'. In the word 'ye**s**' the sound is soft and in the word 'hi**s**' we can describe the sound as hard. We rarely use the '**z**' in English. When your student encounters this letter (**s 2**) he or she must read and pronounce both sounds.

The letters '**ck**' make one sound as in the word 'ba**ck**'.

The letters '**q**' and '**u**' are inseparable in English. The '**q**' represents the sound '**c**' and '**u**' represents the sound '**w**'. Therefore **qu = cw**.

The green letters

The regular English vowel sounds have been printed in green. When your student encounters a vowel; he or she must say the appropriate sound then state: "vowel".
E.g: "a vowel", "e vowel", "i vowel", "o vowel", "u vowel".

Remember!

Your student must read (**Pro**nounce) the letter sounds alone! We will deal with vowel names later. There are those who suggest that these are childish sounds. Nothing could be further from the truth! If you fail to reproduce these basic sounds; the result will be both frustration and stagnation!

Day Month		Day Month		Day Month		Day Month		Day Month	
Pro	kicking k *	Pro	Tongue! th *	Pro	2 sounds s and z	Pro	Together! qu *	Pro	Vibrate lips v *
a		b		sh		p		d	
e		c		d		a		v *	
i		th *		h		e		th *	
o		g		l L		i		h	
u		k		j		o		l (L)	
r		w		f		u		c	
t		sh		s 2		g		m	
y		y		p		b		t	
k *		s 2		z		qu *		ck	
n		ch		m		r		j	
ch		ck		c		f		qu *	

Student must say: "a vowel" "e vowel" "i vowel" "o vowel" "u vowel".
The letters 'c' 'k' (kicking k) and 'ck' (combination ck) make the sound 'c'.

Coach

Spelling

Instructions:

After placing the date in the date grid; work down the columns asking your student to spell the letter sounds in the exercise. It is important that your student is fully aware of the sound you wish him/her to spell.

Reminder: Mutual mouth watching is vital!

Strategy:

1) Coach reads a sound for a student to spell.

2) The student must repeat the sound.

3) The student should then repeat the sound as he or she writes.

4) Tick or dot the grid as necessary. Two consecutive ticks are needed but each tick must be earned on a different day.

Day			Day			Day			Day		
Month			Month			Month			Month		
Spell	qu = cw *		Spell	Kicking k *		Spell	Tongue th *		Spell	Beware*	
a			*ch*			*th* *			*d*		
f			*b*			*e*			*j*		
v			*h*			*v*			*th*		
g			*o*			*l (L)*			*n*		
s			*m*			*w*			*a*		
b			*c*			*i*			*m*		
c			*k* *			*o*			*l (L)*		
t			*s*			*u*			*r* *		
n			*w*			*p*			*w* *		
qu *			*e*			*g*			*ch*		
y			*p*			*d*			*z*		
u			*i*			*t*			*y*		
h			*j*			*r*			*sh*		
sh			*f*			*qu*			*k*		

Important strategy: Spelling exercises require clear speech from coach and student. Make sure that your student is looking at your mouth as you speak. It is also vital that the student replies with each sound. Make sure you can see your student's mouth when he or she replies. The reply must come before attempting the spelling. This strategy must become routine! ***Some students may have difficulty pronouncing the letters 'r' and 'w'. Do not be dogmatic! This is a spelling exercise. If your student can see this page it will be a copying exercise! Note: Demonstrate the use of the tongue with the sound 'th'.**

Coach

Vowel Discrimination (VC)

(VC) = vowel consonant

Students must be able to analyse and express the sounds which they hear. Students with literacy problems can confuse the letter 'b' with the letter 'd'. These problems are, largely, about discrimination between letters which look the same. The distinction between 'g' and 'c' can also cause confusion. As you progress, these problems will disappear. However, the problem with vowels is one of hearing. A difference between vowels can easily be seen on paper but the sounds can be difficult to separate.

Example from Column 1
The coach must say the sound "es".
The student must select the vowel sound only and say "e sound" and then write the letter 'e'.
The coach must say the sound "um". The student must select the vowel sound only and say "u sound" and then write the letter 'u'.

Do not mark until both sounds have been attempted then put a tick or dot in the appropriate box:
One wrong = both wrong!   You must complete each pair. Two consecutive ticks are required.

Please do not use the names of the vowels!

This exercise is concerned with hearing. The coach must be able to see the student's mouth and the student must be able to see the coach form the sounds. In other words: **look at each other!** It is vital that the student verifies the appropriate vowel sound before writing.

Follow the instructions in the coaching box above the exercise on the opposite page.

Day								Day								Day							
Month								Month								Month							

Coach: Read the whole sound to your student. Your student must not spell the whole sound. Your student must **select, say** and **spell** the correct vowel sound alone! One wrong; both wrong! **Each vowel sound in each pair** must be spelled correctly to earn a tick.

es	um							oth	eth							ep	ick						
ig	om							im	ath							ap	ut						
ab	et							uf	ash							og	ap						
ud	ip							ul	im							un	in						
ol	ack							ob	en							oth	ev						
ed	ug							ach	ib							al	id						
ish	ot							eck	osh							eb	ock						
ag	esh							uck	ad							uch	ov						
ush	ick							ub	ich							at	if						
os	af							op	ef							el	up						

Coach

Vowel Discrimination (CVC)

(CVC) = Consonant Vowel Consonant

In the first three-column exercise your student must select the **vowel sound** which has been sandwiched between consonants.

In the second three-column exercise your student will have to select the **vowel sound** from a mixture of (vc) and (cvc) sounds. The instructions are the same as those for the previous exercise.

Strategy:

Student must say and write the vowel sound alone.

Column 1

The coach must say the word "**fad**".

The student must select the **vowel sound** and say "**a sound**" and then write the letter '**a**'.

The coach must say the word "**fell**".

The student must select the **vowel sound** and say "**e sound**" and then write the letter '**e**'.

The coach must say the word "**fog**".

The student must select the **vowel sound** and say "**o sound**" and then write the letter '**o**'.

If your student struggles to understand this process then print the words: '**hat ten sit log fun**' on scrap paper and ask someone to read them for you and demonstrate the process to your student.

On no account must either the coach or the student use the **alphabet names**!

Reminder: We are dealing with letter sounds!

Day Month								Day Month							

Coach: Read the whole word to your student. Your student must not spell the whole word. Your student must **select, say** and **spell** the correct vowel sound alone! **Every** vowel sound in **each group of 3** must be spelled correctly to earn a tick.

fad	fell	fog						as	rip	vet					
fill	bud	top						mop	us	him					
tag	dug	bin						ebb	than	bush					
den	sop	mess						moss	off	fit					
gad	nip	bug						egg	gap	up					
sell	pat	tip						rush	odd	rich					
lop	fan	hug						fen	at	cog					
hop	tell	kit						rum	ill	that					
hog	ban	mud						it	pull	hem					
ten	tog	lab						jog	van	in					

Coach

Read and Pronounce VC (vowel consonant)

The green print reminds your student that these are **vowel sounds**.

Your student must be able to read and spell simple combinations of vowels and consonants. When we read letters alone; the sounds made by them are distinct and separate. To read them in combinations; we slide them together.

Demonstrate the separate sounds of the letters 'a' and 'n' and then demonstrate the sound when they are put together to form the word '**an**'. Use any example from the third column for further demonstrations.

When we form words or sounds this way we remove emphasis from the consonant. It's as if we only say half of the letter.

You can explain to your student that twin consonants, like those in the last column, make the sound of one consonant: The words '**in**' and '**inn**' sound exactly the same!

Day					Day					Day					Day				
Month					Month					Month					Month				
Pro					Pro					Pro					Pro				
af					ep					ob					obb				
ab					en					ol					abb				
ag					el					op					unn				
ad					ef					om					utt				
ap					es					oc					igg				
al					em					og					ott				
ac					ed					ot					eff				
ip					et					ic					emm				
ib					ec					uc					umm				
ig					ug					ud					ogg				
id					ub					un					agg				
im					ut					um					ull				

Coach: Students having difficulty with sounds containing '**b**', '**d**', and '**p**' can have two attempts without incurring a dot. You may find that the letters '**c**' and '**g**' also require two attempts.

Coach

Spelling Two Letter Sounds

Instructions:

After placing the date in the grid; work down the columns asking your student to spell the sounds. It is important that your student is fully aware of the sound you wish him/her to spell.

VC = vowel consonant

Strategy:

1) Coach reads the VC sound for the student to spell.

2) Student repeats the VC sound.

3) Your student should then repeat the VC sound as he or she writes.

Do not allow your student to form the sounds in advance of his/her pencil. The closer a student forms the letters to the sounds they represent; the more accurate will be their spelling. Two consecutive ticks are required to complete each element.

This strategy should become spontaneous!

Day				Day				Day			
Month				Month				Month			
Spell				Spell				Spell			
af				ep				ob			
ab				en				ol			
ag				el				op			
ad				ef				om			
ap				es				oc			
al				em				og			
ac				ed				ot			
ip				et				ic			
ib				ec				uc			
ig				ug				ud			
id				ub				un			
im				ut				um			

Coach

Word Building

This is another important exercise. It will lay down the fundamental method used to read and spell the vast majority of words in our language.

The words and sounds in these exercises are at the core of the code we use: the code which dominates our thoughts, our speech, and the written language we know as English.

Ignore these exercises or fail to give them their due respect and you may use this text as a door-stop!

Ask your student to read the words/sounds in each column; ticking and dotting each element where necessary.

Like the previous exercise, your student must take the first sound on the left as it is read and then he/she should slide it, verbally, into the next sound.

Example:

Column 1:

'i' slides into the 't' to produce the word 'it'.

Column 2:

You must remind your student that twin letters (consonants) make the same sound produced by one consonant.
Note: The words 'in' and 'inn' sound the same.

Inform your student that the box at the bottom of column (2) contains sounds not words.

Columns 3 & 4:

Explain to your student that the letter 'h' is not a true sound. It is there to remind you to breathe out as you say the word.
Practise saying the words 'hat' and 'at' until you are both aware of the tiny breath required to say 'hat' properly.

Day				Day				Day				Day			
Month				Month				Month				Month			
Pro				Pro				Pro				Pro			
y**es**				**T**im				**N**an				**l**ot			
thi**s**				**T**om				Pip				**l**eg			
bu**s**				B**ill**				W**ill**				vet			
plu**s**				**B**en				**D**eb				met			
ga**s**				Sid				**M**att				net			
S**a**m				M**e**g				**N**at				bet			
v**a**t				M**o**ll				**A**nn				but			
Jed				Len				B**e**ss				tub			
R**o**ss				**T**ed				Pat				**B**ob			
Ned				D**a**n				**T**ess				pig			
P**a**m				D**o**n				Jill				rat			
Kim				**K**en				J**e**ss				d**o**g			

Coach: 'Y**es** thi**s** bu**s** plu**s** ga**s**' is a phrase with which your student will soon become familiar. The word plu**s** has been given an early introduction. Do not concern yourself with its repetition.

Coach

Spelling (Encoding)

Ask your student for confirmation of the word you wish to be spelled and then ask him/her to build it as they write it down. Your student must start by writing the first sound followed by the vowel and then the last letter sound.

This might seem tedious but once you are sure that your student is building for spelling, only then can you afford to be less rigid. As the words become longer the more critical this strategy will become.

Problems can only be resolved if you are aware of your student's listening and word building skills. It is not enough to merely tick and dot the words!

Reminder: Mutual mouth watching is vital!

Strategy:

1) Coach reads the word for the student to spell.

2) Your student must repeat the word.

3) Your student should then say the sounds as he/she writes the word.

4) Tick or dot the grid as necessary. Two consecutive ticks are needed for each element.

Do not allow your student to form the sounds in advance of his/her pencil. The closer a student forms the letters to the sounds they represent; the more accurate will be their spelling.

This strategy should become spontaneous!

Day				Day				Day				Day			
Month				Month				Month				Month			
Spell				Spell				Spell				Spell			
fig				cad				cam				had			
tog				wit				mid				vet			
ram				log				pod				can			
hem				peg				jet				sad			
web				pit				jam				rag			
rig				ham				yet				mad			
pun				hen				sag				lad			
tin				sot				pig				bin			
tan				gag				rim				pot			
tab				yen				top				fan			
cog				hug				has				red			
cut				pin				wet				lit			

Coach: This is a spelling exercise! Do not allow your student to see this page!

Coach

Introducing sh

Use scrap paper to introduce your student to the sound 'sh'. Ask your student to repeat the sound 'sh' before starting the first column. The object of this exercise is to use the sounds learned previously to build these words.

Beware!

At the bottom of the first column you will find the word 'shall'. The student who pronounces the word 'shawl /shorl' has substituted the sound of the letters 'a' and the twin letters 'll' for the word 'all'.

Students must use a combination of sounds alone and not words!

This is a good time to make the point!

Remember: **You are building words from sounds and not substituting familiar words for sounds.**

Green letters are vowel sounds

Day			Day			Day			Day		
Month			Month			Month			Month		
Pro	* Beware the word 'all'!		Pro			Pro			Spell		
hip			ish			mush			*ship*		
ship			wish			bush			*push*		
hut			dish			push			*rash*		
shut			fish			lush			*posh*		
ham			ash			hush			*mesh*		
sham			cash			hash			*dash*		
hot			esh			rash			*run*		
shot			mesh			pug			*jot*		
hop			osh			dash			*gash*		
shop			posh			mash			*rug*		
shed			ush			sash			*wish*		
shall *			rush			shush			*shush*		

Coach

The difference between the sounds f and th

It is vital to avoid confusing the sounds 'f' and 'th' in the reading and spelling columns. Make sure that both student and coach emphasise the use of the tongue. It is almost impossible for some students to hear the difference between 'thin' and 'fin' or 'free' and 'three' without an exaggerated demonstration of the use of the tongue.

The two sounds of th

Write the words '**this**' and '**thin**' on scrap paper. Listen to the difference in the sounds of the letters '**th**' in each word.

In the word '**this**' the tongue vibrates against the teeth to form the sound. We can describe the sound made as '**hard**'.

In the word '**thin**' the tongue does not vibrate and the sound we make can be described as '**soft**'.

Spend a short time making these sounds with your student and then proceed with the exercise.

Day					Day					Day					Day				
Month					Month					Month					Month					
Pro	Hard th *				Pro	Soft th **				Pro	th and f				Spell					
th *					th **					that *					*thin*					
the					path					fat					*fin*					
with					kith					gaff					*that*					
within					moth					thin **					*fat*					
rash					Seth					fin					*then*					
them					pith					fog					*fen*					
gash					thug					fish					*than*					
sham					Cath					fob					*fan*					
gush					thud					fig					*this*					
than					Beth					then *					*fuss*					
this					bath					fen					*thug*					

Coach

The sound qu and the Yes Frame

The letters '**q**' and '**u**' in English cannot be separated.
Listen to the sound they make in the word '**qu**it'. The '**q**' cannot make that sound without the assistance of the letter '**u**'. The '**q**' represents the sound usually made by the letters '**c**' and the '**u**' represents '**w**'.

Therefore: qu = cw

The Yes Frame

Ask your student to spell the words in the first spelling column. When this has been done; ask your student to draw a box around the first five words:

yes, this, bus, plus, gas

The first word (**yes**) must then be underlined and you may inform your student that the boxed words represent the '**Yes Frame**'.

Take note of the instructions regarding twin consonants.

Green letters are vowel sounds

Day				Day				Day				Day			
Month				Month				Month				Month			
Pro				Pro				Spell		The **yes** frame*		Spell			
qu				qu**iff**				*yes* *				*rig*			
qu**i**t				**r**ed				*this*				*fig*			
peg				**th**u**d**				*bus*				*set*			
qu**ill**				**n**u**b**				*plus*				*lot*			
leg				**r**ash				*gas*				*push*			
qu**i**p				k**i**t				*then*				*chap*			
la**g**				**y**am				*quid*				*that*			
qu**i**d				**y**et				*que**ll***				*pin*			
gu**m**				**sh**u**sh**				*path*				*ten*			
qu**i**n				c**o**d				*posh*				*men*			
w**i**t				c**o**p				*quip*				*quit*			
que**ll**				**t**a**n**				*hash*				*qui**ff***			

Coach: Spelling columns only: If necessary, assist your student with the letters in bold print: que**ll** qui**ff**. The need for twin consonants will be made clear in later exercises.

Coach

Words Ending in the Sound S

Adding the letter '**s**' to the end of a word might seem like a simple operation but it can obscure the sound before it, thus making it both difficult to hear and spell.

Paired words

Say the word '**rot**' followed by '**rots**'. If you say the word '**rots**', alone, your student will often hear the word '**ross**'! The '**t**' has been buried by the sound '**s**'. To deal with this problem certain words have been paired:

set sets - rat rats - hat hats

Strategy:

Always ask for the single form first.

The Yes Frame

Once more ask your student to frame these words: (**yes this bus plus gas**). After spelling them, ask your student to declare its name: (**The 'Yes Frame'**).

The '**Yes Frame**' contains some of the very few English words which end with a vowel sound followed by a single '**s**'. In most other words which end with a vowel sound followed by '**s**' the letter is doubled:

p**a**ss m**e**ss m**i**ss m**o**ss f**u**ss

Complete the exercise in the usual way. The information above has been given in order to prepare you and your student for the exercises beginning on the pages overleaf.

Green letters are vowel sounds

Day				Day				Day				Day				
Month				Month				Month				Month				
Pro				Pro				Spell				Spell				The **yes** frame *
fans				lad				*ven*				***yes*** *				
pit				nut				*quips*				*this*				
let				nuts				*quins*				*bus*				
lets				thug				*tub*				*plus*				
nuns				fit				*dims*				*gas*				
cat				fits				*shin*				*jog*				
cats				quips				*set*				*sham*				
jet				sun				*sets*				*shim*				
sim				Jim				*had*				*rag*				
mat				shush				*shad*				*thin*				
mats				shot				*rat*				*hat*				
dogs				paths				*rats*				*hats*				

Coach: Both words in the paired frames must be spelled correctly: One wrong = both wrong.

Coach

S or SS

Complete the reading exercise and then ask your student to use the '**yes frame**' for reference.

Before embarking on the spelling columns, inform your student that any word ending with a vowel sound followed by '**s**' (e.g: pa**ss** me**ss** hi**ss** mo**ss** fu**ss**) must have the '**s**' doubled **unless** the word can be found in the '**yes frame**'.

Demonstrate on scrap paper.

Note: The words '**as**', '**us**', '**is**', '**his**' and '**has**' finish with a harder sound; one we would normally associate with the letter '**z**'. That is why these words only have one final '**s**'.

Follow the column guides. Speak clearly.

Day					Day					Day					Day				
Month					Month					Month					Month					
Pro	The **yes** frame *				Pro					Spell	The **yes** frame *				Spell					
yes *					iss					yes *					lot					
this					miss					loss					lots					
bus					uss					this *					quid					
plus					fuss					less					quit					
gas					cats					bus *					fuss					
huss					pigs					runs					rams					
ass					lass					on					pot					
mass					bits					miss					pots					
ess					rips					plus *					Foss					
mess					puts					boss					mess					
oss					cans					lass					let					
moss					dots					gas *					lets					
runs					less					Jess					mass					

Coach

Introducing **ch** and the **Rich Frame**

Demonstrate the sound made by the letters '**ch**' as in '**ch**ip' on scrap paper then work down the '**Pro**' column. Inform your student that the first three words framed in the first column belong to the '**Rich Frame**'.

In later exercises the '**Rich Frame**' and other frames will play their part in the 'Hornet' programme.

The letters in bold print, in the spelling columns, indicate rules that have yet to be taught. You may inform your student that these words end with a double consonant (without earning a dot).

Green letters are vowel sounds

Follow the column guides. Speak clearly.

Day					Day					Day					Day				
Month					Month					Month					Month				
Pro	The **rich** frame*				Pro					Spell	The **rich** frame*				Spell				
rich *					shun					rich *					shun				
such					chad					such					chap				
much					chaff					much					chaff				
chub					shod					chub					shod				
pans					pass					tops					that				
chop					that					chop					man				
chip					man					chin					shell				
chin					shell					chum					pill				
chum					pill					chill					rill				
chill					hat					lag					jug				
chap					hats					chess					hat				
chug					rill					rush					jig				

Coach

Short Sentences

Part 1: Reading

Ask your student to read the short sentences.

From this point, green print will only be used to highlight vowel sounds in particular exercises: to demonstrate new rules: or as reminders of rules learned previously.

Part 2: Spelling (Dictation)

These short sentences are designed to stimulate sequential thinking. Read the sentence to your student who must then repeat it before writing it down.

You may repeat the spelling line, if asked, twice only before incurring a dot. If a dot has been given; break the line into manageable chunks before leaving the exercise.

Day				
Month				
Pro				
The boss is on the bus.				
A lass can pass the hat.				
Mash a mess with moss.				
Quit then push the bell.				
Chop and fill the pots.				
Do not mess with gas!				
Fish for a thin shad!				
A quip can be a pun.				
Yes! The toff has set off.				
Is this such a bad dog?				
Bash pots with mops.				

Day				
Month				
Spell (Dictation)				
This is fish not chips.				
Miss the lips!				
Rush off then quit.				
*This lens is du**ll**.*				
Is that a fat cat?				
Hug the rug.				
Push then pull.				
Shut the lid.				
Quell this fuss.				
Pass rats not pigs.				
Yes this is his mess.				

Coach

Column 1 and 2 CVCC

Your student has already learned to place sounds from left to right in order to read and spell words such as '**tan**' and '**thin**'. We must now expand that process to include an extra sound. There are now 4 elements within the **Pro** columns; each of which has to be read correctly to earn a tick.

Spelling

If your student cannot hear the last two letters of the words in this column, do not be surprised if he/she spells them incorrectly.

Some of the sounds are very difficult to hear and your student may have never heard them before.

This is an exercise in **auditory discrimination** (listening and selecting sounds). It is a difficult exercise for many students but it will sharpen their skills, therefore it is important that you emphasise all the sounds. Be patient!

Green letters are vowel sounds

Day Month					

Pro 4 elements correct to earn a tick

t	ta	tan	tank
b	ba	ban	bank
l	la	lan	land
b	be	ben	bend
l	le	len	lend
i	in	ink	pink
s	sa	san	sand
b	bu	bul	bulk
s	si	sil	silk
r	ri	rif	rift
r	ri	ris	risk
r	ra	raf	raft

Day Month					

Pro 4 elements correct to earn a tick

b	bo	bon	bond
f	fo	fon	fond
g	gi	gif	gift
t	ti	til	tilt
m	me	mel	melt
th	thi	thin	think
l	le	lef	left
l	li	lif	lift
p	pi	pin	pink
g	ul	ulf	gulf
s	se	sel	self
h	hi	hil	hilt

Day
Month
Spell

shelf
jump
lamp
self
melt
think
quilt
bond
thump
risk
champ
pelt

Coach

The sounds ar and or

Once again, there is an important distinction to be made between sounds and words. Students with literacy problems will insert a word which they have memorised as a substitute for a sound. Make the distinction between the sound and the word on scrap paper:

(**ar** = sound **are** = word).

The sound '**or**' and the word '**or**' are the same!

Make sure your student knows the difference between the sound '**ar**' and the word '**are**' before attempting the spelling column!

The Wasp Frame

The letter '**a**' after '**w**' makes the sound '**o**' as in d**o**g. Listen to the sounds in the following words:

w**a**sp - w**a**s - w**a**sh - w**a**nt - wh**a**t - w**a**rm
Follow the column guides. Speak clearly.

Day					Day					Day					Day				
Month					Month					Month					Month				
Pro	sound* word**				Pro	sound and word*				Pro	wasp frame*				Spell	sound* word**			
ar *					or *					yarn					*ar* *				
are **					for					sharp					*are* **				
tarn					corn					charm					*tarn*				
farl					born					horn					*hard*				
darn					pork					shard					*corm*				
harp					form					wasp *					*barn*				
garb					cork					was					*York*				
carp					short					wash					*sharp*				
barb					port					want					*charm*				
ark					torn					what					*torn*				
lark					thorn					warm					*carp*				

Coach: To assist your student silent letters are printed in blue.
Amber letters are there as a warning to students that 'a' after 'w' makes the sound 'o'.

Coach

The short cut X

The Letter '**x**' represents a blend of two sounds: '**c**' and '**s**': see the box below.

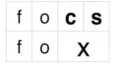

It also represents a blend of the letters '**g**' and '**s**' which is dealt with in the **Word Wasp**.

Amber letters are there as a warning to students that '**a**' after '**w**' makes the sound '**o**'.

Day			Day			Day		
Month			Month			Month		
Pro			Spell			Pro		
ox			*six*			Ask Rex to fix the dish		
fax			*tax*			if a hot mix runs or sets		
Rex			*fox*			on the fat chips. Export		
mix			*vox*			an ox in a thick red box.		
fix			*box*			Get a fax in the bath. The		
six			*fax*			thin fox ran to the forest.		
vex			*Max*			Tax the six men then put		
lax			*vex*			them on the ship. Cash		
fox			*fix*			will vex the taxman. The		
box			*mix*			lad with a sax can upset		
tax			*Rex*			the wasp with the wart.		

Coach

Y can make the vowel sound **i**

Listen to the '**y**' in the following words:

'**y**' makes the sound '**y**' as in '**yes**' and '**yell**'

'**y**' makes the sound of 'i' as in '**happy**' and '**merry**'.

'**Y**' also represents 'i' as in '**fly**' and '**sky**' which is dealt with in the **Word Wasp**.

Column 1 contains the **any/many frame**.

The words '**any**' and '**many**' sound like **eny** and **meny**. They are not phonetically decodable and must be taught as rule breakers. The amber vowel colour warns students to take care with 'any' and 'many'.

In the sentence columns the amber vowels also warn that 'a' after '**w**' makes the sound '**o**'.

Coach: Words in **bold black print** are not phonetically decodable and can be revealed to students and still earn a tick.

Day		any/many frame	Day		any/many frame	Day				
Month			Month			Month				
Pro			Spell			Pro				
yes			*yard*			Polly sat on the holly but				
holl**y**			*berry*			did not think it w**a**s very				
ver**y**			*fussy*			funny. In fact Micky **said**				
yen			*very*			it w**a**s folly and very, very				
yam			*yank*			funny until Polly hit him				
fuss**y**			*yes*			with a very rusty brolly. Six				
sill**y**			*sorry*			happy lads can fix **an**y				
foll**y**			*messy*			sort of buggy but not if the				
yard			*yarn*			lax lad is in a sorry mess.				
any			*any*			W**a**s **a**ny happy lass with				
m**an**y			*many*			**an**y happy lad on a ferry?				

Coach

Words Ending with Vowel Sounds + S / L / F

Example: pass - fell - cuff

We have seen how words ending in a **vowel sound** (not a **vowel name**!) followed by '**s**' usually require the '**s**' to be doubled.

Example: moss - mess - less The exceptions are those words in the **Yes Frame: Yes this bus plus gas**

The same rule applies to words ending with a vowel sound and the letters '**f**' or '**l**'.

Example: off - tiff - toff - gaff - will - sell - dull Rule breakers: nil and pal

The words '**off**' and '**of**' cause problems. When the word '**off**' has been established in your student's vocabulary you may then demonstrate the word '**of**' which breaks the rules.

The rule for '**l**' differs, when the word contains more than one vowel it only requires one '**l**'.

Example: until - compel - dispel - impel - travel - fulfil

Explain the rules to your student as and when you meet them.

Day Month			Day Month			Day Month			Day Month		
Pro	Odd one out *		Pro	pal-nil rule breakers		Pro	Helpful frame *		Spell	Beware! *	
if *			pal			midriff			bus *		
tiff			nil			handcuff			pass		
buff			shell			tariff			dull		
gaff			full			confess			gaff		
toff			riff			compass			yes *		
off			muff			unless			full		
pill			quiff			helpful *			fill		
hill			dull			anvil			fulfil *		
less			ill			cartel			tariff		
pass			quell			dispel			consul*		
boss			fill			artful			fitful *		

Coach: Column 3 contains the 'helpful frame' which reminds students that words containing more than one vowel must end with one l only. Spelling column: Remember the words in the Yes Frame *

Coach

s sh ch ss x followed by es

The object of the '**Pro**' columns in this exercise is to show students that it is not always enough to form plurals by adding '**s**' alone.

Sometimes we have to add '**es**'. The rule is, if the word ends with:

'**s**' (bu**s**) '**ss**' (lo**ss**) '**sh**' (di**sh**) '**ch**' (tor**ch**) '**x**' (bo**x**) the plural is formed by adding '**es**':

bus**es** - fuss**es** - dish**es** - torch**es** - box**es**

Note: The '**es**' plural is pronounced like the sound '**iz**'. The letter '**e**' consistently makes the sound '**i**' as in '**i**nk'.

Although we must speak for spelling there are occasions when we use other tactics: If a student hears '**iz**' at the end of a word it is usually spelled '**es**'. Listen to the ending of the following words:

buses - misses - wishes - marches - fixes

If students miss the double '**ss**', e.g: 'mi**s**es' instead of 'mi**ss**es'; **remind your student to spell the root word first:** spell '**miss**' then add '**es**'.

Take care with the spelling grid:

The difference between the word '**marsh**' and '**march**' may be obvious to you but anyone who needs this book might find the words indistinct. Be sure to emphasise the '**sh**' and the '**ch**' sounds.

Remember to use the formula for spelling:

Say the word clearly.
Your student should then confirm that he/she has heard the word by repeating it. After confirmation your student should then spell the word; saying the letter sounds as he/she is writing: not before, not later, but at the same time!

Day				Day				Day			
Month				Month				Month			
Pro 2 correct to earn a tick				Pro				Spell			
bus	buses			arch				*fox*			
mass	masses			arches				*foxes*			
boss	bosses			marches				*misses*			
fuss	fusses			porch				*buses*			
torch	torches			porches				*losses*			
mix	mixes			larch				*mashes*			
loss	losses			harsh				*marsh*			
miss	misses			marsh				*fusses*			
box	boxes			marshes				*porches*			
mash	mashes			wish				*hisses*			
mesh	meshes			wishes				*torches*			
dish	dishes			rashes				*rushes*			

Coach

Combination ck

When words end with a **vowel sound** followed by a '**c**' sound you must use '**ck**':

p**ack**   d**eck**   qu**ick**   d**ock**   d**uck**

Read and Pronounce

Dates and dots are not necessary for this exercise.

A tick is earned if the words in a row have been read correctly. **Underline** and coach incorrect words by demonstrating the appropriate rules and sounds. **A tick must then be gained on a separate day.**

The words '**any**' and '**many**' sound like **eny** and **meny** and are not phonetically decodable and must be taught as rule breakers.
The amber vowel colour warns students to take care with 'any' and 'many'. It also warns that 'a' after '**w**' makes the sound '**o**'.

Day				Day				**Read and Pronounce**				
Month				Month				in inn egg ebb warm want what				
Pro				Spell				yes this bus plus gas lass boss				
rack				*back*				wish wishes mesh shush chips				
tack				*sack*				path with thin fin then fen fat that				
deck				*peck*				set sets rich such much many				
check				*beck*				elk silk bulk melt felt hilt milk any				
lick				*pick*				born torn harm charm farm alarm				
chick				*quick*				quid quins quip is his as has us				
rock				*lock*				moss fuss hisses misses folly sully				
dock				*sock*				shell sill doll pull gaff tiff toff buff				
duck				*chuck*				confess assess tariff mastiff boxes				
quick				*muck*				canal level compel fulfil peril foxes				

Blue letters = silent Green vowels = sounds Amber = warnings

Coach

Initial Blends

The two letters beginning the words in the exercise columns on the opposite page are called **initial blends.**

Example: **fl** (initial blend) **+ at = flat**. Demonstrate using the word '**flat**' on scrap paper.

Ask your student to listen to each word in the columns. After each word **ask your student to answer with the initial blend alone.**

Example: Coach reads aloud the word '**clip**'. Your student should then say "**cl**". If your student answers correctly; you may tick the box. This is a purely oral exercise.

Listen to the sound of the blend '**tr**' carefully. The '**t**' is barely formed before the full '**r**' sound is introduced. Some students find this blend difficult and try to spell it with '**ch**' or '**chr**'.

Three Letter Blends

The last column contains some three letter blends. The emphasis, with both two and three letter blends, is placed on the last letter. A blend is so named because we blend a small amount of the first sound with a large amount of the last. In other words: **the emphasis is on the last part of the sound**.

The usual two consecutive ticks are required on separate days!

Day				Day				Day				Day			
Month				Month				Month				Month			

This exercise is concerned with listening for sounds. Do not allow your student to see this page.

plant				drum				stick				spend			
cleft				blue				bridge				dwarf			
frog				grass				crisp				twitch			
glad				tress				glum				swing			
slap				prince				slug				drift			
snap				brass				spoon				split			
scam				smart				clip				thrift			
drench				flash				snack				scratch			
trap				plug				scan				spring			
class				glib				flag				shrub			
grub				dross				queen				strand			

Coach: Please note: If you have trouble reading blends you are going to find it difficult to teach them to your student. Go and get help! You will not be the first person not to have been taught them!

Coach

Spelling and Reading Initial Blends

It is easier to teach students to read blends **after** they have been taught to spell them.

Difficulties will emerge with reading because your student will want to pronounce the blend as two separate sounds.

Blends are exactly as they are described: a blend of the sounds represented by the letters. However, that blend is not equal. The first letter has less emphasis than the second and if your student has difficulty you must demonstrate this fact. The blend '**pl**' barely forms the '**p**' sound and places lots of emphasis on the '**l**'.

The rule is: '**demonstrate and persevere**'. Even the most disadvantaged student will 'get there' in the end!

Day					Day				Day				
Month					Month				Month				
Spell *	Both must be correct *				Pro *	Both must be correct *			Pro				
br brim					br brig				brush				
bl bled					bl blot				blog				
cl clip					cl clip				class				
dr dram					dr drag				dress				
fr from					fr frill				frog				
gr grim					gr grass				grim				
pr prom					pr prod				press				
tr trip					tr trash				trim				
sc scar					sc scan				scarf				
pl plan					pl plan				plank				
sm smell					sm smog				smell				
sn snap					gr grip				grab				

Day					
Month					
Spell *	Both must be correct *				
sp spot					
st stick					
sw swig					
tw twin					
cr crust					
thr throb					
str strap					
squ squint					
spr sprint					
spl splash					
shr shrub					
scr scrub					

Day					
Month					
Pro *	Both must be correct *				
sp spin					
st stop					
sw swim					
tr tram					
cr cross					
thr thrip					
str struck					
squ squill					
spr sprat					
spl split					
shr shrink					
scr script					

Day			
Month			
Pro			
spun			
stamp			
swill			
tramp			
cramp			
thrift			
strim			
squid			
sprig			
splint			
shrank			
scrimp			

Day Month							Day Month							Day Month								
Pro							Pro							Spell *		Both must be correct *							
brink							thank							cr	crushes								
stilt							wilt							tr	tramps								
stink							think							sc	scans								
stock							clock							sw	swells								
graft							drift							gr	grand								
shank							shrank							shr	shrimps								
scrimp							scamp							thr	thrusts								
thrift							swift							spr	sprits								
spark							stark							squ	squids								
still							distil							str	strips								
shall							rental							spl	splats								
twin							drink							scr	scraps								

Coach

Sentences:

These short sentences have been designed to stop students using the context as a means of guessing rather than building.

Read and Pronounce

Dates and dots are not necessary for this exercise.
Words in **bold black print** are not phonetically decodable and can be revealed to students and still earn a tick.

A tick is earned if the words in a row have been read correctly.
Underline and coach incorrect words by demonstrating the appropriate rules and sounds.
A tick must then be gained on a separate day.

The words '**any**' and '**many**' sound like **eny** and **meny** and are not phonetically decodable and must be taught as rule breakers.
The amber vowel colour warns students to take care with 'any' and 'many'. It also warns that 'a' after '**w**' makes the sound '**o**'.
Blue letters = silent   Green = sounds

Read and Pronounce

Ma**ny** silly fishes swim in ponds when lasses stand on a box in the rushes.

Insist that shrimps, shrink or trav**el two** yards for a drink from a well in Bath.

Carry a shred or split the end of a strap to form a link in the hard brass traps.

Was it a risk that six, soft, pink, dishes will shrink if held in front of a hot lamp.

This will sink **a**n**y** rats that l**ive** in the shrubs but not the cats that hunt them.

Impress, thrill and thrust a staff then strip thin shreds from thorns and fronds.

Thresh the fresh short grass into **m**a**ny** lush scraps with a shard of glass.

The sprit w**a**s split in a swell as the mist from the glen fell on the black deck.

Thrushes rush to the bushes if a fox blushes and passes the marshes.

Lard is hard until it is put in a hot pan and splashes the scraps of fresh fish.

A chub is a fish as is the shark, the shad and garfish but not a mink or a pug.

Coach

Simple Sentences for Reading and Spelling

Sentences or phrases will not always make sense to coach or student. It is important that your student does not guess the word by analysis of the context but uses the skills learned, thus far, to build words from sounds.

The spelling exercise will be difficult because students will have to put the words in the correct order as well as spell them correctly. This exercise is about developing a sequential memory.

You must read the sentence or phrase to your student.
Your student must repeat the sentence then write it.
You may repeat the spelling line, if asked, twice only before incurring a dot. If a dot has been given; break the line into manageable chunks before leaving the exercise.

Amber letters are there as a warning to students that 'a' after 'w' makes the sound 'o'.
Blue letters = silent Green vowels = sounds

Day			Day		
Month			Month		
Pro			Spell (Dictation)		
Thwart the frogs with warts.			*Sprint then squint.*		
Pens in boxes have quills.			*Plan to mix in a yard.*		
Barry splashes in the bath.			*Stand on the strand.*		
Is that a tendril on the drill?			*Distil and fill the flask.*		
Stamp on the damp grasses.			*Do not stress the mess!*		
Discuss a stressful mess.			*Contest, fix and invest.*		
Relax and abscond in Kent.			*Tell Jimmy if Ted is hot.*		
Fifty muddy frogs jump.			*Confess and compress.*		
The harsh sun can scorch.			*Milk can help the Hulk.*		
Is the torch in the porch?			*A hot plant can wilt.*		

Coach

The Letter k before i - e - y

In English words the letter 'c', when placed before the letters 'e', 'i' or 'y', makes the sound we normally associate with the letter 's'. If we need to form a 'c' sound before 'e', 'i', or 'y' we must use the letter 'k'.

Take note of this in the **Pro** columns and demonstrate the rule to your student.

The letters are highlighted in bold green print to demonstrate when and where to use the letter 'k'.

Strategy:

At this stage you can tell your student that they must use the letter 'k' to form the 'c' sound if they hear it before an 'e', 'i' or a 'y' or if they hear it at the end of a word.

Day			Day			Day			Day		
Month			Month			Month			Month		
Pro			Pro			Pro			Spell		
kit			mil**ky**			s**ki**ll			*kin*		
can			**k**ith			scum			*cusp*		
keg			bul**ky**			skip			*Kent*		
cull			**k**ilt			scalp			*kith*		
kid			carp			s**k**ep			*kilt*		
cob			**k**iln			scar			*carp*		
kiss			cult			s**k**in			*skip*		
car			**k**elt			Scot			*skin*		
kin			cost			skid			*skep*		
s**k**inny			**K**ent			por**ky**			*scalp*		
Ken			cusp			s**k**ink			*scab*		

Coach
Stressing the Vowels in Two Syllable Words

When spelling infrequent words, your student will spell that which they hear. What else can they spell? The final **vowel sound** in many of these words remains unstressed. You must make sure that they are stressed when you ask your student to spell them.

Listen to the bold green **vowel sounds** in the following words:

emblem - organ - mental - tendon - dragon

The final vowels are unstressed and all sound the same but you must make sure that these vowels are heard. The 'o' in 'dragon' must sound like the 'o' in 'dog'; the 'e' in 'emblem' must sound like the 'e' in 'egg' and the 'a' in 'mental' must sound like the 'a' in 'ant'.

However, once your student has spelled the word it must then be repeated in normal speech:

Schwa symbol/unstressed vowels: ə

The symbol used for unstressed letters is commonly known as '**schwa**' and this is what it looks like: **ə.** We have replaced that symbol with amber letters.

ardent = ardənt   organ = orgən
mental = mentəl

Coach: The **Pro** columns are for you to correct the student's pronunciation which will involve unstressing many final vowels.
It is vital that this procedure is followed.

Day					Day					Day					Day				
Month					Month					Month					Month				
Spell					Spell					Pro					Pro				
shank					*orbit*					absent					emblem				
vanish					*crank*					orbit					extend				
random					*dragon*					ambit					expand				
signal					*vendor*					intend					brandish				
intend					*ambit*					expel					vanish				
compost					*implant*					unjust					varnish				
problem					*sordid*					import					vandal				
ardent					*mental*					ardent					vendor				
organ					*harden*					fulfil					blemish				
emblem					*sharpen*					organ					selfish				
until					*garden*					until					implant				
tendon					*gambit*					mental					tendon				

Syllable Division

Having tried many ways of dividing words for reading, it became clear that a single, universally appropriate, method of dividing a word was not going to be found.

Coach

Syllable Division

This exercise is designed to help students analyse longer words.

Students must be able to divide longer words into manageable chunks.

Remember!

Your student must read these sounds or words in order that you can monitor his/her attempts and work out any weaknesses. By doing this your student is also less likely to guess.

Unstressed vowels carry amber warnings **to remind students that these vowels should not be stressed.**

pregnant = pregnənt   methodist = methədist

Pro instructions for unstressed vowels are on **page 76**

Coach: Work from left to right. All five words and/or sounds must be read correctly to earn one tick.				Day Month							
Work from left to right ------------------------------------>											
> pop	popcorn	gum	gumdrop	droplet							
> tar	tarnish	varnish	harness	marches							
> stag	stagnant	grem	gremlin	pregnant							
> corn	Cornish	self	selfish	brandish							
> trip	triplet	kin	kinship	hardship							
> clasp	unclasp	helm	helmet	pelmet							
> ask	mask	unmask	Skipton	Skegness							
> ast	aston	tonish	astonish	admonish							
> shr	shrap	apnel	rapnel	shrapnel							
> pest	pestil	ilent	pestilent	prominent							
> op	optim	imist	optimist	pessimist							
> op	opsim	simath	opsimath	methodist							

Day					Day					Day					Day				
Month					Month					Month					Month				
Pro					Pro					Pro					Spell				
thrips					masses					contact					*kismet*				
shrimp					bosses					impact					*seldom*				
shrift					glasses					compact					*tendril*				
thump					torches					conduct					*tarpon*				
truck					insist					consist					*sprat*				
splash					resist					content					*unlevel*				
farl					sprag					portent					*stress*				
gulch					porches					habit					*spindrift*				
Welsh					clumps					enlist					*harness*				
stark					clamps					orbit					*spectrum*				
risk					fresh					mugwump					*insist*				
frisk					crush					tepid					*thrips*				

Coach: **Spell** and **Pro** instructions for unstressed vowels are on **page 76**

Read and Pronounce

Pro	/	Pro	/

Sixty fat thrips **were** sent to drink milk from ramsons in a dark glen. In the garden, often left, slugs will have scant respect for parsnips or radish. Clumps of bushes, corms and rushes, thorns, stems and grasses, protect garden insects, larks and thrushes. Which red raft rushes in the rapids and thrills the sharp stork from York? A shovel from a hovel will diminish the pile.

A strict thin, pink, shrimp was not content to miss the dentist and repent. Give short shrift to a thin shrimp that shrinks from a dish of squid, scraps and strips of chips. Starfish and lots of frogs respond to limpets. **Were** the carp fond of the bugs that dwell in ponds? Dogs are kept as pets but not hornets. Marlin, with thin red fins, flash past fishes that gasp.

Coach: **Underline** and coach incorrect words by demonstrating the appropriate rules and sounds. **A tick must then be gained on a separate day.** Blue letters = silent

Coach

Syllable Division

This exercise is designed to help students analyse longer words.

Students must be able to divide longer words into manageable chunks.

Remember!

Your student must read these sounds or words in order that you can monitor his/her attempts and work out any weaknesses. By doing this your student is also less likely to guess.

Unstressed vowels **will carry** amber **warnings to remind students that these vowels should not be stressed.**

connect = cənnect   solvent = solvənt

Pro instructions for unstressed vowels are on **page 76**

Coach: Work from left to right. All words and/or sounds must be read correctly to earn one tick.				Day Month			

Work from left to right --------------------------------->

>	ect	nect	onnect	conn	connect			
>	act	ract	tract	ontract	contract			
>	uct	duct	truct	struct	construct			
>	ict	rict	strict	district	constrict			
>	rel	relin	quish	inquish	relinquish			
>	ject	inject	sect	inspect	spectrum			
>	barr	ass	barrass	embarr	embarrass			
>	tess	tress	undress	press	express			
>	rip	ript	script	onscript	conscript			
>	vent	sent	olvent	invent	solvent			
>	calp	scalp	impel	scalpel	propel			
>	kip	skip	skep	skeg	Skegness			
>	port	import	ress	fortress	stress			

Day				Day				Day				Day			
Month				Month				Month				Month			
Pro				Pro				Pro				Spell			
admit				normal				apartment				*often*			
insist				Cornish				admonish				*Cornish*			
Morton				selfish				insistent				*animals*			
Norton				pretend				consistent				*stiff*			
habits				instant				optical				*still*			
rabbits				constant				optimum				*informal*			
Trunket				defend				informal				*segments*			
fortress				animals				important				*important*			
report				obsess				fragment				*selfish*			
armpit				oppress				demolish				*instant*			
adorn				formal				Flemish				*constant*			
upset				ingress				segments				*remnant*			

Coach: **Pro** and **Spell** instructions for unstressed vowels are on **page 76**

Pronounce

Mr. Anton Hamlet Horton rents an apartment in West Morton. In a modest flat, the oddest up for rental, Mrs. Hilda Trunket Snatt had problems with Anton Hamlet Horton's cat. In March the residents of the garden pond, of which the cat was fond, did end up stiff and still upon Hilda's kitchen steps. Mrs. Trunket Snatt had often felt that if the cat would sport a bell; then any animal that dwelt within the garden's bonds would have less stress and lots of fun. Expel from the fens, strands and fronds that stand in the ponds. **Do** many thrushes rush to crush shells on the canal bank? Clamp fifty lamps and expect to get cramp in the legs. Charm the farm animals that live in a barn. Alarm bells and odd smells mark the start of a march across a park. Send a Cornish friend to a ford and report to the fortress. If the flag is torn it cannot adorn the front of a porch. Arrest a man and his friend from Holland and then send many unhappy chaps to imperil the consul from Hull.

Coach: **Underline** and coach incorrect words by demonstrating the appropriate rules and sounds. **A tick must then be gained on a separate day.** Blue letters = silent   Green = sounds

Coach

Difficult Sounds (ng)

The '**ng**' word ending is difficult to hear, read and pronounce. It is the addition of the vowel before it which allows students to deal with the structure and complexity of the sound.

Green letters are vowel sounds

Page 89

If you hear '**lenth**' and not '**length**' then a dot has been earned. You may have to insert the '**g**' fully by saying the word in three parts:

'len-g-th'

Many people will find these words difficult to hear and say. Persevere but avoid making your student anxious.

Note: The exercise will be counter-productive if the end product is anxiety.

| Day | | | | | | |
| Month | | | | | | |

| Pro 4 elements correct to earn a tick | | | | | | |

a	an	ang	bang			
sang	rang	pang	gang			
fang	clang	hang	tang			
i	in	ing	sing			
fling	thing	ling	cling			
ring	sling	sting	string			
o	on	ong	song			
long	gong	thong	throng			
along	among	strong	prong			
u	un	ung	sung			
lung	bung	rung	slung			
flung	stung	strung	sprung			

| Day | | | | |
| Month | | | | |

| Pro | | | | |

Limpets cling to rocks.			
Bats hang in barns.			
Angry wasps can sting.			
Ring the bells and sing.			
Cling to a raft or a ring.			
Stand on the rung.			
It sprang from the trap.			
Bang hard on a gong.			
Dugongs swim in a pond.			
String it with strands.			
Gangs of rats jump ships.			
Is it clinging or longing?			

Day					Day				Day				
Month					Month				Month				
Spell					Pro Both must be correct				Spell				
sang					wing	winging			*blessing*				
sing					ringing	longing			*crossing*				
song					bring	bringing			*fussing*				
sung					swinging	king			*resting*				
bang					pressing	throng			*throng*				
ring					dressing	oblong			*strong*				
long					messing	prong			*fasting*				
lung					shortest	longest			*trusting*				
gang					thin	thing			*jesting*				
ling					softest	hardest			*bring*				
gong					lasting	dusting			*string*				
bung					trusting	resting			*thing*				

Day					Day				Day				
Month					Month				Month				
Pro Both must be correct					Pro				Spell				
bang	banging				flung				*among*				
bending	standing				rung				*amongst*				
hang	fangs				sting				*rang*				
pang	sprang				stung				*sprang*				
rang	gang				clung				*landlord*				
stand	lend				sprung				*casting*				
bend	mend				len...				*costing*				
mending	ringing				leng...				*length*				
lord	landlord				length				*lengthen*				
hanging	landing				lengthen				*strength*				
kissing	missing				strength				*strengthen*				
warming	wanting				strengthen				*pressing*				

Pro and **Spell** instructions for unstressed vowels are on **page 76**

Coach: Work from left to right. All five words or sounds must be read correctly to earn one tick.				Day Month						
Work from left to right -------------------------------->										
>	spr	ing	spring	sing	springing					
>	fast	fasting	sting	stinging	clinging					
>	arch	march	ment	parch	parchment					
>	ash	cash	cashing	smash	smashing					
>	pect	ospect	prosp	rospect	prospect					
>	ress	ressing	pressing	impress	impressing					
>	Brid	idling	Bridling	lington	Bridlington					
>	plant	implant	planting	planet	planks					
>	elf	self	unself	selfish	unselfish					
>	shr	shrink	shrinking	thinking	stinking					
>	quest	inquest	esting	questing	requesting					
>	int	quin	quint	squint	squinting					

Coach: **Pro** instructions for unstressed vowels are on **page 76**

Read and Pronounce

Inspect the prospects and respect the insects that inject a sting. Insist that a hornet is given a warning or it will obstruct and reject attempts to land the catfish on the banks of the Trent. Planting bushes amongst the rushes was sending fish across the vast pond to the marshes. Fish will shrink from warm, strong and dark drinks but will not reject the singing which starts at Lent. This shark is selfish but his friend the squid is not. Crabs and molluscs are still on the shelf but mullet can stick in the gullet when bits get left in the fillet. Strong smells and shrinking ponds are starting to bring the fat rats to the flats but the strength and length of the contract will act to stop the rot. Marching on planks in a marsh will send **women** to harass the top brass. Discuss the rust on the arches but not if the car is in the park. Assist a shrimp to squint and shrink at the contents if the dog snarls at a stick.

Other Information

The letters '**ch**' in most European languages translate to the sound we usually associate with '**sh**': para**ch**ute, blan**che**, ma**ch**ine, **Ch**ampagne. French words which have entered our language: stau**nch** and lau**nch** etc, retain the French pronunciation.

The '**nch**' sounds of English words of a similar structure are hardly discernible from the French: Listen to the sound of '**nch**' in lau**nch** and again in lu**nch**.
The problem is not with the pronunciation: The sound is so close to '**nsh**' that anyone with a literacy problem is more likely to spell '**bransh**' rather than '**branch**'.

Coach

ch after the Letter n can say sh

The letters '**ch**' can make the sound '**sh**' if they follow the letter '**n**'. People who do not have literacy problems take this point for granted. Listen to the sound of '**ch**' in the word '**French**'.

Example:

lunch = lunsh   bunch = bunsh

Draw your student's attention to the rule in the reading columns.

The plural form of words ending in '**ch**' observe the same rule as words ending '**s**', '**ss**', '**sh**', or '**x**'.

E.g: bus**es** - boss**es** - bush**es** - lunch**es** - box**es**

Day					
Month					
Pro					
Fre**nch**					
be**nch**					
clash					
ste**nch**					
fresh					
mesh					
te**nch**					
brash					
bra**nch**					
trash					
ra**nch**					
lush					

Day						
Month						
Pro Both must be correct						
lu**nch**	hush					
hu**nch**	mush					
mu**nch**	crush					
cru**nch**	push					
pu**nch**	fish					
fi**nch**	pi**nch**es					
co**nch**	bu**nch**es					
crashes	cli**nch**					
marches	porches					
torches	harsh					
marshes	fli**nch**es					
gushes	wi**nch**es					

Day					
Month					
Spell					
French					
crunch					
bunch					
stench					
torch					
bushes					
wishes					
harsh					
march					
larch					
starch					
punch					

Day							Day						Day					
Month							Month						Month					
Pro Both must be correct							Pro						Spell					
frost	trust						squinting						*quench*					
pinches	drench						winches						*quenches*					
drenches	quest						winching						*hornet*					
quench	quenches						chant						*squint*					
morning	grant						chanting						*squinting*					
granting	branches						crunching						*blending*					
lunching	hornets						branching						*sling*					
flashing	flinching						brunches						*slung*					
targets	trusting						scorch						*standing*					
quenching	tending						scorching						*prospect*					
spending	lending						passing						*obstruct*					
branches	squint						passes						*object*					

Day			Day			
Month			Month			
Pro			Spell (Dictation)			
pinching things that shrink			*squinting and flinching*			
hisses then kisses the bosses			*Jack has lost his lunch!*			
thinking of dusting the benches			*dishes the dumplings*			
torches in the dark arches			*starches not scorches*			
classes of larks in a form			*thinks but not shrinks*			
Drench the men on the bench.			*hands are not wet*			
Pinch or punch the card.			*pinches the finches*			
welding the start of the branch			*clenches the fists*			
singing a song to the **women**			*Film the damp lamp.*			
marching along with a band			*welding not melting*			

Coach: You may repeat the spelling line, if asked, twice only before incurring a dot. If a dot has been given; break the line into manageable chunks for spelling before leaving the exercise.

Coach

Silent t after a Vowel Sound

Strategy: Before starting this exercise, write the **vowel sounds** on paper.
Remember: The **vowel sounds** are:

a - ant
e - egg
i - ink
o - on
u - up

Read each vowel sound to your student. Ask your student to repeat each sound with the addition of the '**ch**' sound.

Example:

coach:	"a"	student	"ach"
coach:	"e"	student	"ech"
coach:	"i"	student	"ich"
coach:	"o"	student	"och"
coach:	"u"	student	"uch"

Spelling

The previous examples are of **vowel sounds** followed by the '**ch**' sound. If your student hears a word ending with a **vowel sound** followed by a '**ch**'; he/she must insert a silent '**t**' between the **vowel sound** and the '**ch**', unless the word can be found in the '**rich frame**', which now contains the word '**which**'. The word '**which**' carries a silent '**h**' and it can be taught at this stage.

Examples:
match - sketch - pitch - notch - hutch

Strategy:

When your student has completed spelling the words from the '**rich frame**' ask him/her to draw a box round the words. This can then be used for reference.

Day			Day			Day			Day		
Month			Month			Month			Month		
Pro	Rich Frame *		Pro			Pro	ch = sh *		Spell	Rich frame *	
rich *			twitch			Dutch			*rich* *		
such			snatch			clinch *			*such*		
much			batch			scratch			*much*		
which			ketch			starch			*which*		
fletch			sketch			match			*scotch*		
itch			stretch			winch *			*thatch*		
thatch			latch			larch			*stitch*		
ketchup			snitch			theft			*catch*		
kitchen			ditch			witch			*match*		
switch			flitch			cleft			*stretch*		
clutch			hatch			pitch			*sketch*		
crutch			stitch			bunch *			*kitchen*		

Day				Day					Day			
Month				Month					Month			
Pro				Pro	Both must be correct to earn a tick.				Spell			
scotch				sketching	fletches				*itches*			
hatches				pennant	darting				*hitches*			
invent				switching	matching				*matching*			
latches				Thatcham	Mitcham				*catching*			
tram				scratches	starting				*twitching*			
trammel				twitching	plump				*stitches*			
batches				conforming	jolting				*conforms*			
imperil				stretches	hatching				*informs*			
vetch				conform	submit				*banging*			
bunting				catching	bolting				*clanging*			
blotch				hotchpotch	springing				*scratches*			

Coach: Instructions for coloured letters page 15 - Unstressed vowels page 76

Day				Day				
Month				Month				
Pro				Spell				
Miss and then catch a bus.				*Scratch a hatch with a fork.*				
Lift up the stiff latches.				*Catch a bus on the Strand.*				
Can it sniff then snatch?				*Pick a lock with a bent pin.*				
Which witch cast the spell?				*The land is stark in the dark.*				
Were stitches made of silk?				*Which witch cast the spell?*				
Scratch the lids with a stick.				*Sharks swim and often grin.*				
Such a rich snark can swim.				*Hatch the eggs in the nest.*				
Were sharks having lunch?				*Which ducks swim in ponds?*				
Sketch the larks in the park.				*Hatch a plot to catch a cat.*				
Switch to the ditches.				*Stop the rot with lots of tar.*				

Coach: You may repeat the spelling line, if asked, twice only before incurring a dot. If a dot has been given; break the line into manageable chunks for spelling before leaving the exercise.

Coach: Vowel sounds are printed in green. Ask your student to find, pronounce and tick the vowel sounds: 'a' as in 'apple', 'e' as in 'egg', 'i' as in 'ink', 'o' as in 'on', 'u' as in 'up'.

c	a	d	c	e	f	p	v	i	p	c	b	o	n	c	u	p	c	i	t	c	u	w	c	x	a

Coach: Vowel names are printed in red. Ask your student to find, pronounce and tick the vowels names: 'a' as in 'ape', 'e' as in 'even', 'i' as in 'island', 'o' as in 'over', 'u' as in 'unit'.

r	i	d	c	a	i	r	c	f	e	c	a	t	i	c	u	e	c	o	c	a	g	a	c	i	o

Coach: Ask your student to find, pronounce and tick the vowel sounds and vowel names below. There are 21 vowels in this exercise of which 9 say their name and 12 say their sound.

f	r	i	t	p	e	o	f	u	n	o	t	i	v	a	k	l	a	t	a	l	o	w	d	a	n

u	h	j	o	e	t	p	u	l	k	g	i	o	l	b	n	h	g	a	p	i	p	z	f	u	a

Read and Pronounce Together!

Read the sentences with your student. The earlier your student understands the difference between the sounds and the names of the vowels the easier your task will be!

The green letters are vowel sounds; the red letters are vowel names and the blue letters are silent.

My name is a; you can hear me in Avon, brave and late.
My name is e; you can hear me in Edith, these and theme.
My name is i ; you can hear me in Isla, mile and mine.
My name is o; you can hear me in Omar, bone and robe.

My name is u; I have 2 names you can hear them in unit, cute, mute, ----- blue, crude and true.

To hear the difference close your eyes and say: use, muse then blue and rude.

My name is e; I am the chief assistant. I often bully other vowels.

Coach

Vowel Identification

The difference between **vowel sounds** and **vowel names** is at the heart of WASP teaching strategies.

The exercise on the opposite page is designed to teach your student to discriminate between sounds and names.

There are four words in each line. After each word ask your student to identify the central vowel in each word.

The **vowel names** are highlighted in red. The **vowel sounds** are highlighted in green.

Example: The first row column one:

| bone | back | dim | tile |

Coach reads: "**bo**ne."
Student replies: "**o name**" then writes the letter '**o**'.

Coach reads: "**ba**ck."
Student replies: "**a sound**" then writes the letter '**a**'.

Coach reads: "**di**m."
Student replies: "**i sound**" then writes the letter '**i**'.

Coach reads: "**ti**le."
Student replies: "**i name**" then writes the letter '**i**'.

Beware: **This exercise is concerned with vowel discrimination. Spelling the entire word will undermine the exercise completely. Your student must spell the vowel sound or vowel name only.**

Vowel Discrimination		Day	Month					Vowel Discrimination		Day	Month				

Coach: Your student must **identify** and **spell** the vowel only!

bone	back	dim	tile					like	must	grebe	stake				
gum	cute	tend	theme					pest	tome	frost	plush				
mule	rust	make	slap					nude	cash	pike	ship				
limp	dime	posh	pole					cube	dine	cone	lost				
grip	gripe	glebe	dwell					fame	split	test	sale				
gulp	rude	sham	shame					smile	lobe	clan	mush				

Coach: Do not let your student see this page. This is a **hearing** exercise!

sad	fade	rush	duty					dupe	fast	drake	stoke				
spike	gift	beck	Pete					slave	clove	file	flop				
slam	wade	slop	slope					code	breve	task	wilt				
dust	mute	felt	Steve					fuse	node	vale	slime				
swell	here	trip	tripe					glum	June	mess	flask				
soft	mode	gale	clash					prod	strike	fist	clump				

Coach

Vowel Identification

Our letters are divided into vowels and consonants. Both vowels and consonants have **sounds** and **names** but the vowels alone can say their **names** in English.

Consonant names are not necessary in English and only serve to confuse students with literacy problems.

Vowel names, on the other hand, are extremely important.

In many words the vowels: **a e i o u** can stand alone, without the help of other vowels, and say their **name**. However, most often, the vowels assist each other to produce their **names**.

Example: With assistance: g**a**me s**o**le
Without assistance: m**o**st m**i**ld

In column 1 the vowels saying their **name** have been printed in red. The word '**do**' breaks the rules. It has been inserted because we need to explain the '**do-go**' frame. The word '**to**' also breaks the rules.

Strategy: After your student has spelled the words '**do**', '**does**,' '**go**' and '**goes**' place them in a frame. This is the '**do-go**' frame (rhymes with **Hugo**).

Explain that English words ending in '**o**', must be extended with '**es**' much the same as words ending in '**s**', '**ss**', '**sh**', '**ch**' and '**x**': bus**es** - miss**es** - dish**es** - bunch**es** - box**es** do**es** - go**es**

This rule opens the way to the correct spelling of many words including the word '**does**', without the need to rely on mnemonics.

Day				Day				Day				Day			
Month				Month				Month				Month			
Pro	rule breakers *			Pro	add es *			Pro				Spell	do-go Frame *		
so				smash				into				do *			
he				pushes				undo				does			
she				vellum				indigo				go			
do *				does *				hello				goes			
to *				goes *				sling				truth			
go				host				slang				most			
me				both				logo				post			
no				post				Ruth				undoes			
be				most				truth				she			
I				ghost				hornet				ghost			
we				clutches				cornet				both			

Day								
Month								
Pro *Both must be correct*								
grind	find							
hind	mind							
toll	gold							
told	sold							
old	hold							
do	does							
go	goes							
going	doing							
blind	fold							
roll	rind							
child	mild							
wild	host							

Day							
Month							
Spell	rule breaker *						
roll							
rolling							
post							
most							
*do *							
does							
doing							
go							
goes							
going							
old							
sold							

Day							
Month							
Spell							
hold							
gold							
told							
stroll							
strolling							
golden							
fold							
folding							
holding							
bind							
mind							
finding							

Read and Pronounce

Holding a rolling pin, strolling along the strand while folding **two** blindfolds, I was told, is a mindless thing to do. Going to a bank, doing the shopping, marching along, swimming long lengths, can give him strength if he is fit and well. Fishing and angling are much the same to a fish. If she does the correct thing then we can put it behind us but not if the harsh cold pinches the nose. If it is so, then we shall hold then fold a sling before he goes in front of the bench. **Two** wasps will want to wash in warm water and hornets are not very happy to have a bath if the water is cold or very hot. English mustard, is very strong and can make **you** want **to** sneeze.
Did the **woman** stretch **two** matching patches of scarlet cloth before she went to fetch **two** lengths of gold cloth to form a cold compress for the bold child with **two** gold rings. Remind a bull that stamping on grass compresses it into a formless mess which is a problem and not helpful to the kids from Bridlington, **who** arrive on the bus that runs on a mix of pink petrol and gas.

Coach: Underline and coach incorrect words by demonstrating the appropriate rules and sounds. **A tick must then be gained on a separate day.** Blue letters = silent   Red = names
Amber = warnings: 'a' after 'w' makes the sound 'o'. Unstressed vowels **Page 76**

Coach

The Silent Assistant e (Mute 'e')

The power of the vowel usually moves from right to left!

Although the previous exercise has demonstrated that vowels can say their name without help from other vowels; in most words, we can describe vowels as 'lazy'!
To get them to utter their name they usually need assistance. If we add the letter 'e' to the end of the word 'tap' we form a new word: 'tape'. The 'silent assistant' (e) thrusts its power into the vowel 'a' but in so doing it loses its own power and becomes silent. The assistant 'e' prods the vowel into action.

Imagine the vowel holding a needle which is long enough to pass through one consonant and prod a vowel into shouting its name.

However, it only has the power to get through one letter (consonant). The word 'tape' has one 'p', if it had two then the word would not

make sense. In English 'tappe' is a meaningless collection of letters and the assistant is totally idle.

All vowels, **but particularly the 'e'** have the power to influence the sound of other vowels.

Strategy:

In the first **Pro** column the sounds have been printed in green and the names in red. The silent assistant 'e' has been printed in blue.

In the **Spell** column the order of the words has been switched, at random, in order to prevent students from guessing.

In the third column all the vowels have assumed their normal guise and your student will have to work out the vowel names according to the structure of the word: An 'e' on the end will be silent and the vowel will say its name.

Day				
Month				

Pro 2 correct earns a tick				
grip	gripe			
grim	grime			
trip	tripe			
sham	shame			
spat	spate			
shad	shade			
cod	code			
ban	bane			
nod	node			
slim	slime			
scrap	scrape			

Day				
Month				

Spell 2 correct earns a tick				
mate	*mat*			
dam	*dame*			
mad	*made*			
slop	*slope*			
tale	*stale*			
hope	*hop*			
glad	*glade*			
robe	*rob*			
spin	*spine*			
mop	*mope*			
tope	*top*			

Day				
Month				

Pro 2 correct earns a tick				
sprung	thud			
quilt	thane			
brine	thug			
bring	theme			
mode	crone			
sprit	spade			
prong	hunting			
sprite	trite			
probe	bide			
grape	hulk			
thrive	trope			

Coach

Syllable Division

Sounds, like words, observe the rules!

This exercise is designed to improve your student's ability to read syllables (chunks of letters forming a sound) from left to right.

Coach: Work from left to right. All five words and/or sounds must be read correctly to earn one tick.				Day								
				Month								

Work from left to right --------------------------------->

> elt	pelt	peltat	tate	peltate								
> spit	spite	espit	espite	respite								
> dane	undan	undane	mundan	mundane								
> con	oncret	concret	oncrete	concrete								
> rem	trem	treme	extrem	extreme								
> anch	ranch	franch	ranchise	franchise								
> omp	comp	ompose	compos	compose								
> rust	frust	rustrate	frustrat	frustrate								
> ill	illust	strate	ustrate	illustrate								
> ect	lect	ectrod	lectrode	electrode								
> est	stim	estim	stimate	estimate								
> cul	ulmin	minate	culmin	culminate								
> capad	scapad	escap	scapade	escapade								

Day						
Month						
Pro 2 correct earns a tick						
grade	crate					
theme	choose					
those	grime					
slide	silk					
pride	spent					
prime	charm					
cope	hone					
ride	same					
hate	late					
thong	drive					
strive	graft					
state	throng					

Day				
Month				
Pro				
incline				
mundane				
repose				
transpose				
compose				
complete				
combine				
relate				
escape				
provide				
missile				
hostile				

Day				
Month				
Spell				
made				
tide				
mash				
hope				
tame				
chine				
chime				
came				
these				
take				
lint				
make				

Read and Pronounce

She can pose for a snap and dispel the smell. She will stitch the **clothes**

for the man with the patches **who** sits on the pitch and munches his lunch.

Does an incline, combine, define, refine and devise the rise of the bold,

wild, child as she compiles a file and wins prizes for matching despatches?

One cannot condone the tones of the cornet, the horn and the trombone.

Can **one** condone a lone throne made from bone for one clone alone?

Harass the lass on the cliff if the tariff for the gas is **enough**. **Who** went

flashing along the drive in a blue car to confront the shocking truth? If

the bloke can cope with a telescope, the black kite can escape the fate of

the late Mr. Snipe, **who** did not strike the man with a pike. The shrike with

stripes can spit at a rude Duke if he expects the cute bride on the ride to

give tributes to the mute student, in the black and blue kilt, from Bute.

Coach: **Underline** and coach incorrect words by demonstrating the appropriate rules and sounds. **A tick must then be gained on a separate day.**   Blue = silent   Red = names

Coach

More Mute e

Sometimes the mute 'e' will directly affect the vowel to its left without having to pass its power through a consonant. You will find such words in the first column.

Adding the '**s**' to some words may mean that your student fails to recognize the presence of the mute 'e'. As your student becomes a better reader and speller these difficulties will disappear.

Coach: To assist your student, silent letters are printed in blue.

Amber letters are there as a warning to students that 'a' after '**w**' makes the sound 'o'.

Day				Day			Day			Day			
Month				Month			Month			Month				
Pro				Pro			Pro			Spell		do-go Frame *		
foe				complete			brigades			*lie*				
Joe				conquest			prints			*lies*				
toe				propose			invades			*tie*				
due				prospect			sprints			*ties*				
vie				contrite			inclines			*do **				
cue				vanquish			squints			*does*				
tie				wasp			impedes			*go*				
pie				wash			shrinks			*goes*				
lie				want			devotes			*doing*				
argue				what			stinks			*going*				
die				watch			intones			*toes*				

Day			Day			Day	
Month			Month			Month	
Pro		Tongue *	Pro		Tongue *	Spell	Tongue *
swift	spine		tilth *			*impose*	
stove	clove		untie			*ties*	
gave	stave		rose			*compose*	
spike	shrill		roses			*intend*	
thank	thrill		compose			*kindness*	
thane	jibe		composes			*child*	
alone	home		impose			*states*	
splash	dine		imposes			*plates*	
method	filth *		dispose			*depth* *	
depth *	globe		disposes			*filth* *	
strobe	trade		compost			*tilth* *	

Read and Pronounce

Tie lines to a spike and compose a note and send a complete theme to the
man with the shrill tones. An insane white stag in the forest will **lose** the
hinds, if it lags behind, in the cold driving snow. Send for the man with the
shrill tones to remind the hinds to show kindness to old ruminants.
Expel the ruminants from the barn and send **one** to **Alysidex.** Wasps, ants
and hornets belong to the same family. "I cannot tell a lie," the Empress
said but as she spoke **her** nose began to **grow**."Do not suppose," she said
at length, to the **only** drone that clung to the throne, "to disclose that it will
lengthen **because** of the depth of filth on the throne." **Only** one lone
clone alone from Athlone told the truth to those inside the state **of** Alysidex.
Does **one** mind the lies that combine at times to promote her decline?
Next to the compost, the depth of the tilth is quite important for a garden.

Coach: **Underline** and coach incorrect words by demonstrating the appropriate rules and sounds.
A tick must then be gained on a separate day. Blue = silent Red = names Green = sounds
Unstressed vowels **Page 76**

Coach

The Two Names of u - oo and yoo

In the words '**fl**u**te**' and '**r**u**de**' the vowel 'u' makes an 'oo' sound (as in m**oo**n).

In the words 'u**se**' and 't**u**be' the vowel 'u' makes the same sound with the addition of a 'y' sound: 'yoo'.

Beware: Because of the confusion arising from 'look and say' methods: your student may want to insert the words '**you**' and '**who**'.

Red letters are vowel names

Day				Day				Day				Day			
Month				Month				Month				Month			
Pro	u says oo			Pro	u says yoo			Pro	mixture			Spell	mixture		
sue				use				enthuse				*unit*			
flute				useful				ruse				*unite*			
clue				fuse				rune				*prune*			
rude				amuse				rebuke				*brute*			
true				acute				allude				*include*			
crude				cube				refuse				*compute*			
glue				tune				obtrude				*intrude*			
rule				mute				occlude				*crude*			
blue				tube				protrude				*avenue*			
lute				dupe				fluke				*tribute*			
plume				fumes				flume				*blue*			

Day					Day					Day					Day				
Month					Month					Month					Month				
Pro					Pro					Spell					Spell				
brute					bath					*glue*					*abuse*				
spell					dispute					*spume*					*confuse*				
dispel					both					*clue*					*obtrude*				
conclude					impute					*rude*					*amuse*				
napkin					cost					*going*					*useful*				
intrude					jute					*impute*					*exclude*				
distaff					lost					*tube*					*astute*				
pollute					puke					*true*					*tribune*				
spilth					butane					*futile*					*resolute*				
resolute					most					*goes*					*continue*				
include					June					*does*					*dispute*				

Day						Day					
Month						Month					
Pro						Spell (Dictation)					
demonstrates the facts						*Is the franchise French?*					
inundates with trash						*a conscript in the trenches*					
complicates the tasks						*Does the Empress tell lies?*					
culminates or frustrates						*Contribute to the dispute.*					
probes with electrodes						*Stretch the springs.*					
takes some respite						*Dispel and fulfil the thrills.*					
estimates or implicates						*Estimate the time for lunch.*					
includes the mundane						*trombones and trumpets*					
go goes going gone						*She escapes from a kitchen.*					
compose for trombones						*makes a mastiff munch*					

Coach: You may repeat the spelling line, if asked, twice only before incurring a dot. If a dot has been given; break the row into manageable chunks before leaving the exercise.

Coach

The Two Names of U

As we have stressed earlier: the vowel 'u' has the luxury of having two **names**: the sound '**oo**' (as in m**oo**n) and the sound '**yoo**'. Eg: r**u**de = **oo** f**u**se = y**oo**

Beware: The problem with 'u' is that it can alter the sound of the letters to its left. The letter '**d**' before the 'u' can sound like the letter '**j**' and a '**t**' before a '**u**' can sound like '**ch**': **duke / juke - tube / chube**.

Some students will struggle to pronounce the words **dune, tube** and **dupe** but they will serve as a reminder when we deal with other words which share similar problems.

Blue letters = silent Green = sounds Red = names
Amber = warnings: unstressed vowels
Instructions for unstressed vowels Page 76

Day				Day				Day				Day			
Month				Month				Month				Month			
Pro	Beware! *			Pro				Pro				Spell	Beware! *		
une				g**h**ost				m**a**rv**e**l				*dune (d not j) * *			
dune *				grime				cling				*tube (t not ch) * *			
ube				wept				stretches				*dupe (d not j) * *			
tube *				swept				emboss				*ghost*			
upe				flung				funding				*skilful*			
dupe *				grip				risking				*most*			
scutch				gripe				unkempt				*nematode*			
drench				spark				magn**a**te				*constrict*			
tr**u**th				shard				drifting				*strike*			
vulture				prone				enclose				*emboss*			
sketch				prime				inflate				*stride*			

Coach

Losing the Mute e

We have stressed that the vowel 'e' has the greatest potential for changing other vowels from sounds to names. However, all vowels have that potential.

If we remove the 'e' and add the letters 'ing'; the vowel 'i' becomes the assistant which lances the consonant 'k' and makes the 'a' say its name: take - taking.

When we add 's' to the word 'take' the mute 'e' remains active but silent and we still hear the vowel name: takes.

All the words in each row need to be **read** correctly to earn a tick.

All the words in each row need to be **spelled** correctly to earn a tick.

Blue letters = silent Green = sounds Red = names

Day							Day						
Month							Month						
Pro 3 correct earns a tick							Spell		a correct row earns a tick				
drive drives driving							*drive drives driving*						
slope slopes sloping							*thrive thriving*						
like likes liking							*glide glides gliding*						
hide hides hiding							*take takes taking*						
dine dines dining							*computes computing*						
mine mines mining							*hopes hoping*						
stoke stokes stoking							*times timing hiding*						
make makes making							*grates grating*						
ride rides riding							*braking joking*						
wake wakes waking							*bakes baking*						

Day		Day		Day	
Month		Month		Month	
Pro		Pro		Spell	
astute		dating		*children*	
groves		escaping		*escaping*	
thrives		escapes		*trading*	
plants		impede		*impede*	
trends		impedes		*control*	
friend		control		*stating*	
states		bold		*kinship*	
stating		truth		*flames*	
late		mild		*hold*	
latest		wild		*child*	
dates		child		*uphold*	

Day				Day				Day				
Month				Month				Month				
Pro	Tongue *			Pro	Tongue *			Spell				
catch				vanish				depth *				
glasses				varnish				ketchup				
holding				conch				fragment				
folding				Spanish				segment				
text				thinking				inquest				
next				drinking				conquest				
context				marching				landing				
quell				credit				standing				
sketch				prompt				demolish				
filth *				handcuff				rebel				
quench				depth *				stitching				
trench				propel				spending				

Day					Day					Day					Day				
Month					Month					Month					Month				
Pro					Pro					Spell					Spell				
most					conclude					*glue*					*do*				
post					intrude					*blue*					*does*				
shrub					mistake					*true*					*doing*				
glue					inflate					*clue*					*elf*				
throb					inflating					*prude*					*shelf*				
blue					devote					*astute*					*help*				
tube					devoting					*dispute*					*kelp*				
tune					impose					*jute*					*quote*				
do					imposing					*flaking*					*quite*				
does					compose					*go*					*self*				
go					dispose					*goes*					*golf*				
goes					reporting					*going*					*jest*				

Day			Day			Day			Day		
Month			Month			Month			Month		
Pro			Pro			Spell	Frames *		Spell		
adipose			tribe			*yes* *			*shine*		
franchise			polite			*this*			*shining*		
morbid			deprive			*bus*			*grade*		
electron			legume			*plus*			*siskin*		
eldritch			alive			*gas*			*grades*		
impress			relate			*rich* *			*grading*		
thatching			relates			*such*			*file*		
ingrate			slates			*much*			*filing*		
viscose			revive			*which*			*smile*		
cathode			hopes			*do* *			*smiling*		
implode			scope			*does*			*likes*		
contrite			dates			*go*			*liking*		
plinth			dating			*goes*			*taking*		

Coach

The Sound ure

The '**ure**' doesn't cause a problem in words such as '**cure**', '**pure**', and '**manicure**'. It is only when a '**t**' comes before '**ure**' that students have difficulty:

pic ture   struc ture   den ture

The '**t**' before '**ure**' almost sounds like a '**ch**' sound.
Ask your student to use '**t**' before '**ure**' and not a '**ch**'.

For those students who fail to grasp the concept above; you will have to revert to speaking for spelling and stress the '**t**' sound:

pict ure   struct ure   dent ure

However, once your student has spelled the word it must then be repeated in normal speech.

Monitor and correct the pronunciation in the **Pro** columns.

Beware: Normally, we form a '**sh**' sound at the beginning of the word '**sure**'. We cannot do this when speaking for spelling. It might seem awkward but you must form the '**s**' when speaking for spelling.

Day				Day				Day				Day			
Month				Month				Month				Month			
Pro				Pro				Spell				Spell			
ure				picture				*ure*				*picture*			
cure				posture				*pure*				*structure*			
pure				pasture				*cure*				*fracture*			
manure				puncture				*sure*				*pasture*			
secure				denture				*insure*				*venture*			
endure				fracture				*unsure*				*posture*			
impure				culture				*secure*				*denture*			
immure				structure				*impure*				*ligature*			
sure				vulture				*manure*				*adventure*			
unsure				rupture				*procure*				*future*			
insure				mixture				*demure*				*sculpture*			
demure				rapture				*closure*				*capture*			

Day		Day		Day		Day	
Month		Month		Month		Month	
Pro		Pro		Spell		Spell	
indenture		impress		*old*		*delude*	
obscure		comp**a**ss		*bold*		*stature*	
capture		tranqu**il**		*wold*		*de*mure*	
manicure		c**o**mp**e**l		*gold*		*divides*	
f**u**ture		midriff		*scaffold*		*enslave*	
sculpture		mastiffs		*strong*		*inhale*	
premature		squinch		*longing*		*extract*	
pedicure		stench		*strength*		*inspect*	
procure		stretches		*length*		*object*	
insecure		pitchfork		*dispose*		*does*	
departure		eleg**a**nt		*front*		*doing*	
fixture		oblong		*abjure*		*goes*	

Read and Pronounce

Are dentists mending dentures with egg-white and glue? If the bite is not **right** then polish the gums with cold vinegar and resin. If the taste is odd; prod the lips with the end of a shaving brush and do not make contact with hot or cold drinks. If grapes are ripe you can be **sure** you will not endure a nasty taste. Divide and then rule is a game we have to endure to procure for a mugwump a life of high profits. Squint at a vulture; but if it winks back then save **your** strength for the long length of time it takes to capture the fort from the friends of those **who** went North. Include, in despatches, those **who** sport patches on floppy hats. As the mustang goes loping along, we think of the future and if we might capture the wild, wise, and strong. Can we procure a cure for mumps, and things that go bump in the night? It is cold in the frozen lands north of Alysidex. The very severe wind was chilling noses and mitts **were** thick and frostbite a constant peril.

Coach: **Underline** and coach incorrect words by demonstrating the appropriate rules and sounds. **A tick must then be gained on a separate day.** Blue = silent Red = names Green = sounds

Coach

The Sound ire

Listen to the sound made by the letters 'ire' in the word fire'. Demonstrate the spelling of the sound 'ire' on scrap paper then begin the exercise.

At the end of the county names (column 3), the sound 'ire' has been reduced to little more than a 'sh' sound.

Allow your student to use the sound 'ire' as in 'fire' to pronounce the words marked with an asterisk * and amber print then offer the correct pronunciation and mark with a tick.

Pro and Spell instructions for unstressed vowels
Page 76

Day	Day	Day	Day
Month	Month	Month	Month
Pro	Pro	Pro	Spell
ire	rust	aspire	*dire*
tire	pundit	culprit	*spire*
retire	desire	conspire	*shire*
trust	ambit	thrills	*tires*
spire	inspire	respire	*retire*
crust	gambit	peltate	*Yorkshire*
mire	admire	transpire	*shorten*
dust	pulpit	mandate	*length*
dire	umpire	Yorkshire *	*lengthen*
must	trunk	pancake	*admire*
shire	empire	Flintshire *	*inspire*
just	crank	mistake	*conspire*

Day					Day					Day				
Month					Month					Month				
Pro					Pro					Spell				
fire					obscure					*fire*				
firing					obscures					*firing*				

Coach: Ask your student to notice how the assistant '**e**' disappears: fi**re** / fi**ri**ng - cure / curing.

admire					obscuring					*cure*				
admiring					endure					*curing*				
planting					endures					*obscure*				
conspire					enduring					*obscures*				
conspiring					hopscotch					*obscuring*				
infuse					th**e**rap**i**st					*confuse*				
infusing					mindful					*confuses*				
confuse					aspire					*confusing*				
confusing					aspiring					*handful*				

Read and Pronounce

If **you** want, intend or aspire to climb the steps within the spire that stands alone beside the mire, then be sure to hold a rope or line to ensure that just bad luck or fate divine does not conspire or combine to cast **you** into the abyss sublime. Withstand the cold on the high scaffold and if **you** endure then find a spot **where** the sand is soft and jump. If **your** feet begin to sink in the black mud; do not attempt to wash them in the kitchen sink. Mum will be most upset, if she is watching you make black marks upon her **once** white washing. If she is angry she will want a therapist to expel the red storm. No excuse will get you off! Be mindful that flight and not fighting is often very useful but being sorry might also be helpful. Watch the wasps with a telescope and watch for a **woman** who will cure any demure lass.

Coach: **Underline** and coach incorrect words by demonstrating the appropriate rules and sounds. **A tick must then be gained on a separate day.** Blue = silent Red = names Green = sounds Amber = warnings: 'a' after '**w**' makes the sound '**o**'. Unstressed vowels **Page 76**

Coach

The Sound ore

Listen to the sound made by the letters '**ore**' in the words 'sn**ore**' and 'c**ore**'.

Demonstrate these sounds on scrap-paper before beginning the exercise.

Day								Day								Day							
Month								Month								Month							
Pro								Pro								Spell							
ore								impact								*gore*							
more								define								*adore*							
restore								before								*before*							
strike								refine								*store*							
core								implore								*implore*							
astride								sublime								*restore*							
tore								shore								*more*							
beside								grade								*spore*							
bore								chore								*score*							
besides								degrade								*chore*							
sore								score								*snore*							
abides								inflate								*shore*							

Day							Day							Day						
Month							Month							Month						
Pro							Pro							Spell						
deplore							gore							*implores*						
vote							goring							*restores*						
adores							bore							*empress*						
voting							boring							*pinafore*						
cores							hatchet							*ignoring*						
devote							snore							*sprinting*						
ignore							snoring							*adores*						
devoting							ignores							*gores*						
impose							ignoring							*quill*						
spore							emblem							*tranquil*						
imposing							distaff							*snoring*						
galore							spores							*saving*						

Pro	/	Spell (Dictation)	/
By the sea shore she sold sea shells.		*Finish the chore.*	
She chose to dispose of those red roses.		*Argue the toss with the bosses.*	
The squire from the shire will not retire.		*Respect a request.*	
Can he endure such obscure cures?		*Request a rest on a long ride.*	
Are you sure the ship goes to the shore?		*Tell the men with guns to go home.*	
Request that a pest is moved from the class.		*Be bold and take hold.*	
Is adipose tissue an issue at the clinic?		*Decline the wine.*	
Hold on to **your** hats in the wild wind.		*Does a pest take a rest?*	
Do not contemplate the fate of the glass plate.		*Endure the cure.*	
Invigorate, separate, isolate and medicate.		*Compress the mess.*	
Combine, entwine, propel, incline or decline.		*Deplore the gore.*	
Rebuff hot tubs of suds for a cold compress.		*She ignores his snores.*	

Coach

The Need for Twin Consonants

The power of the vowels moves from right to left and we can see this happening with the silent assistant 'e'. However, in most words, the vowel has only got the power to go through one consonant. Look at the following words:

dinner diner

We use twin consonants in the word di**nn**er ('**nn**') to stop the 'e' from making the letter 'i' say its name.

All vowels have the power to alter the sounds of preceding vowels. That is why the word 'dine' can be changed to 'dining' when the assistant 'e' has been removed.

dine din (e) ing = dining

The word 'wishes' has two consonants between the vowels 'i' and 'e' and therefore the 'i' can only say its sound and not its name. Certain words can break the rules but most English words obey them.

Read and Pronounce
Twin letters (consonants) stop the power of the vowel!

slop slopping slope sloping slopes

bid bidding bide biding bides

pin pine pines pinning pining

slid slides sliding riding ridding

slim slime slimming trimming

win wine wines wining winning

hop hopping hope hopes hoping

sit site siting sitting hitting sites

cut cute cutting mute mutes lute

cot cotton button rotten note noting

fuss fuse fussing fusing fuses infuse

sham shaming shame shamming

file files filing filling

till tiling tilling tile tiles

twin twine twining twinning

tot tote toting totting

lop lope loping lopping topping

mope mop moping mopping

rob robe robbing robing robes

plan planning planing

kit kite kitten kites

scrap scraping scrapping scrape

Coach: **Underline** and coach incorrect words by demonstrating the appropriate rules and sounds: **A tick must be gained on another day.** Blue = silent Red = names Green = sounds

Read and Pronounce
Twin letters (consonants) stop the power of the vowel!

driving the buses for friends	shaping and shipping the baking
sending and spending the savings	likes dangling the hand-line
licking and then sticking the stamps	pining for home and pinning the dress
minding the child on the steps	ridding the park of dogs not rides
going quite wild in the waves	taking the time to reflect on the picture
saving the stamps for the chap	mining for gold in the north of Alaska
hoping not moping for luck	hitting the hissing snake with a stick
holding and folding the dresses	planning to plane the plank with a blade
sitting and sketching the kitten	pinning the cotton ribbons on the poles
coping with the depth of the pond	fussing and infusing the tea not the milk
not running and robbing the gold	confuses, refuses and defuses the fuses
thrives in cold running water	sliding and slipping along with a sled

Coach: **Instructions for coloured letters page 15 -** Unstressed vowels **page 76**

Day Month Spell							Read and Pronounce	
		2 correct earns a tick					Pro	/
loping lopping							Hitching a ride from his kitchen in Hitchin, Fred	
hoping hopping							Mitchum was switching buses to go to Dorking.	
taping tapping							After pinching his arm, when passing a farm, he	
planing planning							could not stop himself from twitching and itching.	
linking sinking							A grebe from Old London Park spoke to a vampire	
fusing fussing							some time after dark: "make no mistake, if you drink	
voting singing							from the lake your smile will drive off the shark".	
mining hunting							Smell, consume and dispute but don't be rude.	
smelling selling							Let's drink from the well until it's time to have lunch.	
vending lending							Drape the bulk of the hulk in a silk dressing and	
hiding hidden							incline the bovine to fire the milk into the basin. You	
joking skimming							can snarl at the consul and fake a smile for a child.	

Coach: **Underline** and coach incorrect words by demonstrating the appropriate rules and sounds.
A tick must then be gained on another day. Blue letters = silent   Red letters = names

The Word Wasp literacy manual gives a more in-depth analysis of the soft 'c' rule but for now your student only needs to understand why we use the letter 'k'.

Coach
The Use of ck and the Soft C

The letters 'ck' are used to protect a vowel from the power of other vowels in exactly the same way as twin consonants protect vowels from each other. We cannot double the letter 'k' in English. Apart from a few exceptions, we only use a 'k' before 'i', 'k', or 'y'.

The problems arise when you want to protect the vowel using double 'cc'. **Example:**

baccing = bacsing   correct spelling = backing

Line 1 (below) does not pose a problem but in **line 2** the letters 'i', 'e' or 'y' after a 'c' make it form the 's' sound and that is why we must use the letter 'k' before an 'i', 'e' or 'y' if we wish to retain the 'c' sound.

1) cat cot cup cash: c = c
2) city cinder cell fancy: c = s

If we did not use 'ck' we would not be able to protect the vowel when adding the letters 'ing' or 'er' after words like 'back' to form 'backer' or 'backing'.

Day					Day					Day					Day				
Month					Month					Month					Month				
Pro					Pro					Pro					Pro				
ba**ck**					take					ma**k**e					spi**k**e				
b**a**ck**i**ng					taking					ma**c**e					spi**k**es				
bake					tack					la**k**e					spi**k**ing				
b**ak**i**ng					tacking					la**c**e					li**c**e				
stock					stake					bi**k**e					**K**ent				
st**ock**i**ng					staking					spi**c**e					**c**ent				
stoke					puck					Mi**k**e					wink				
st**ok**i**ng					puking					mi**c**e					win**c**e				
lick					slake					**I**ke					win**c**ing				
li**ck**i**ng					slaking					i**c**e					win**k**ing				
li**k**e					slack					pu**k**e					lan**c**e				
li**k**i**ng					slacking					pu**c**e					lank				

Blue letters = silent Green = sounds Red = names Amber = warnings: c = s

Early Problems

Initially, some of our students experienced difficulties with this exercise but it did not take long before they began to enjoy the thinking process which it was designed to encourage!

Coach

The Use of the Soft c ck and k

The reading exercise alone contains words which operate the soft 'c' rule. The spelling columns invite the appropriate use of the letters 'ck' or 'k'.

Day									Day								
Month									Month								

Pro 3 correct earns a tick									Spell		2 correct earns a tick						
fake	face	faking							*lick*	*licking*							
faces	fakes	facing							*link*	*linking*							
stock	stoking	stocking							*shock*	*shocking*							
bank	back	bake							*fork*	*forking*							
pink	stake	stack							*shrink*	*shrinking*							
rakes	races	raking							*crank*	*cranking*							
race	rake	racing							*slink*	*slinking*							
stoke	snack	snake							*clunk*	*clunking*							
baking	banking	barking							*hike*	*hiking*							
brake	brace	braking							*choke*	*choking*							
braces	brakes	bracing							*frisk*	*frisking*							
smoking	lacking	linking							*cluck*	*clucking*							

Day				
Month				
Pro				
sketching				
quidditch				
lunches				
child				
shrill				
graceful				
distress				
process				
sheriff				
staff				
porches				
marches				

Day				
Month				
Pro				
shredding				
hopping				
hopeful				
hoping				
structure				
empire				
restore				
sprinting				
springing				
flaking				
skink				
Kilbride				

Day				
Month				
Spell				
himself				
helpful				
backing				
dandruff				
matchless				
goldfinch				
flaking				
skimming				
brandishes				
embarrass				
Skegness				
deprive				

Read and Pronounce

Embrace a stick; shake it at a snake before packing the testy children off to bed.

Place the rice and rise above the ramparts. Capture a squirrel before it jumps off

a branch. Displace flakes of skin as dandruff and fit a tight hat. Mistakes at sea

can be costly. Adventures with **your** dentures can lead to poor fixtures and odd,

unorthodox, dental structures. Hire the man from the park to tend **your** nature

garden and watch for starlings but not for the buntings that sing in the branches.

Parking a car is a bad chore when driving from London, Hampshire or Yorkshire.

Until the buses bring masks; choking fumes will make bold kids ill in Notting Hill.

Blocking paths with carts and bikes stop artists from making tracks in the sand.

Passing amulets helps those behind desks to remind a sentry to hide problems.

Take stock of the fact that stacking the boxes and staking a post will slacken the

lines so slake the lime if it makes a loss. Visit the bosses when Vikings are here.

Coach: **Underline** and coach incorrect words by demonstrating the appropriate rules and sounds. **A tick must be gained on another day.**   Blue = silent   Red = names
See unstressed vowels **Page 76**

Coach

The Digraph er Makes Two Sounds

Listen to the sounds made by the letters '**er**' in the following words: '**f**er**n**' and 'butt**er**'

The '**er**' sound in the word '**f**er**n**' is longer than the '**er**' sound at the end of the word 'butt**er**', which is little more than a grunt. Within a word, '**er**' can be described as the **long** sound of '**er**' and at the end of a word it can be described as **short**.

Schwa symbol/unstressed vowels: ə

The symbol used for unstressed letters is commonly known as '**schwa**' and this is what it looks like: **ə** biggə bettə buttə. We have replaced the symbol with amber letters.

Strategy:

Demonstrate the difference by writing the following words on scrap paper.

Long - 'er'   **term   perk   fern**
Short - 'er'   **bigg**er **bett**er **butt**er

Say the two sounds of '**er**' after each other until you are fully aware of how they differ then start the exercise.

Green letters = sounds   Red letters = names   Blue letters = silent

Day			Day		Day		Day	
Month			Month		Month		Month	
Pro			Pro		Spell		Spell	
skipper			terminate		*butter*		*convert*	
blender			invert		*blister*		*divert*	
letter			kerbstone		*mother*		*terminal*	
stretcher			internal		*brother*		*internal*	
thicker			convert		*faster*		*perfect*	
fender			stern		*hacker*		*servant*	
thinner			merchant		*miser*		*merchant*	
diner			thermal		*spinner*		*perching*	
dinner			chervil		*splinter*		*chervil*	
splinter			jerk		*chatter*		*person*	
miner			servant		*rider*		*perks*	
scatter			serpent		*stretcher*		*Gertrude*	
backer			perfume		*killer*		*hermit*	

Read and Pronounce

Does the serpent smell the perfume and then bite the sternum of those that bother to hide the butter from a miser? A perfect person will gather herbs and give them to the hermit but not to Kermit. The latter, a frog, a former tadpole I presume, speaks English. **Some** thermal springs will bring hot water in summer or winter to none of those that live close to the volcano. The sister of the farmer was the partner of the brother **who** was holding the banner in a very silly manner for the dervish with the spanner. Perform the rites in spite of the mites that infest the person **who** gave the sermon to the diver named Herman.

In the pasture, getting faster, taking a sniff at the aperture made by the mole, the child with the satchel, was not absconding from Alysidex to concoct an excuse for the insolvent state of his torpid friends from the Essex fens. The severe stench from the trench made Bertram wince as he drank doses of the stuff which his mother often makes when illness strikes children living in the Yorkshire hills. The bus, when due, often accrues blue hats from those girls who will imbue you with the truth in summer. A score, he was sure, would make Ruth adore or desire the man on the shore.

Read and Pronounce

Does a dose of a tincture come close to a cure for impure drinks that often stink like an old kitchen sink? The price of wine often combines with the decline of those inclined to a life of crime. Bill was a criminal, Jack was a lad, and telling the Old Bill has made him such a cad. Immature overtures often result in a tumult of abuse. Ignore the rules if you wish to be unwise and to never grasp a true understanding of English spelling.   After hitching a ride from a kitchen in Hitchin, and switching buses, Fred Mitchum, **couldn't** stop itching when shaving. A bold grebe from Old Lister Park, spoke to a vampire one night after dark: "Make no mistake, if you drink from the lake, **your** face will upset the shark!" The score is one nil so his pal with the severe problem can no longer inspire the rest of the empire to compose then retire before the end of the match. Some interesting prose was composed and exposed to a panel from across the channel.

Coach: **Underline** and coach incorrect words by demonstrating the appropriate rules and sounds. **A tick must be gained on another day.   See** unstressed vowels **Page 76**

Other information

Many high frequency English words originate from the language used by the tribes of the North German Plains. The final 'e' on the end of many of these words was stressed but that stress has fallen from use.

Words like 'come' (German - komme) still retain 'e', but it has long since been silenced.

Coach

The Gone Frame

In the words in the **Gone Frame** the **silent** e has lost its power. These words end in the letters 'one' or 'ome'. '**Something**' is a compound word (two words joined together) but the root word is 'some'.

Your student will be confused by the word '**one**' (the number), which is unique, but this is the best time to learn how to spell it.

Beware: There are two sounds:

'one' as in 'gone' and 'one' as in 'bone'.

Blue letters = silent Green letters = sounds Red letters = names
Amber letters = warning

Day				Day			Day		
Month				Month			Month		
Pro 2 correct earns a tick				Spell			Spell		
stone	lone			done *			under		
clone	home			condone			over		
bone	trombone			come *			clone		
zone	prone			some *			clover		
tone	throne			one *			rover		
drone	condone			someone *			thunder		
gone	shone *			throne			blunder		
come	some			undone *			scone		
welcome	someone			welcome *			dome		
income	something			income *			home		
done	undone			none *			gone *		
one	none			shone *			intone		

Day				Day				Day				Day			
Month				Month				Month				Month			
Pro				Pro				Pro				Spell			
gloss				shelter				miner				*formless*			
impress				butcher				does				*scruff*			
hardback				banker				dose				*rebuff*			
midriff				embark				clinging				*rolling*			
kinship				structure				bluffing				*implicate*			
none				shrill				strung				*obese*			
gone				satchel				string				*uniform*			
sure				carnival				stringer				*carnival*			
pressure				duress				singer				*blanching*			
demure				uniform				friend				*scratch*			
umpire				glimmer				unlike				*fletcher*			
transpire				shimmer				scrunch				*butcher*			

Pronounce

In the forest some were welcome but not those gangs who were lopping the Ash. Someone tell me the name of the shameful dame who sometimes arrives after five, when she has a mind? Exposing one's nose to temperatures so cold that frost will form nasty nasal stalactites which will result in an acute loss of friends. The sons of retrograde farmers from Dorset have become satchel snatchers in Kent so lift a latch to a sneck and expel the stone ammonites within. Has he done the job or has he gone to get some jam? Can he have one of the vessels, if she smiles at the servile **women**? Does an umpire or artist take doses of black snuff before a match in Halifax begins? Travel in planes but do not imperil those that expel or dispel bold artists from the sculpture park. Scatter the scratchings left by the fletcher and expect a welcome from the children **who** dwell under perspex. Place a space under a fancy blanket to exclude the dude from the truth. The time has come but none have gone to Bath. The sun **once** shone on the welcoming shores but not anymore.

Coach: **Underline** and coach incorrect words by demonstrating the appropriate rules and sounds. **A tick must then be gained on a separate day.** See unstressed vowels **Page 76**

Coach

English Words Cannot End with the Letter V

Have you ever wondered why some people live after touching live wires? The question posed is concerned with the words 'live' and 'live' and has nothing to do with electricity.

There are many reasons for this: Hundreds of years ago two forms of writing dominated early scholarship: one rounded (Celtic) and the other, more angular, (Italic or Roman). The letters 'u' and 'v' could be confused therefore people began to mark 'v' by following it with an 'e'. Remind your student to remove the 'e' when the word gets extended: **love - loving**

Watch out for the '**Move Frame**'! Move, prove, improve, approve. Approve breaks the rules because it should not be necessary to double the '**p**'!

Please note! The letter 'v' cannot be doubled in English because two 'v's make a '**w**'.

Green letters = sounds   Red letters = names

Day					Day					Day					Day				
Month					Month					Month					Month					
Pro					Pro					Pro					Spell					
give					live					parting					*involving*					
have					live					quiver					*solving*					
love					liver					bidding					*quiver*					
above					diver					cover					*shivering*					
dove					hover					revolve					*loving*					
shove					clover					twelve					*shoving*					
forgive					shiver					jumper					*hamper*					
solve					thrive					starter					*jumper*					
involve					wasp					move					*move*					
valve					want					prove					*prove*					
delve					warm					improve					*improve*					
shelve					was					approve					*approve*					

Day			Day			Day			Day			
Month			Month			Month			Month			
Pro			Pro			Pro			Spell			
shivering			done			muster			*carve*			
quivering			itself			duster			*starve*			
hovering			himself			embark			*nerve*			
covering			above			emboss			*swerve*			
pampering			glove			spilling			*valve*			
hampering			shove			shaping			*involve*			
none			olive			what			*solve*			
gone			having			wash			*twelve*			
something			giving			testing			*disrupt*			
one			bluster			stress			*abrupt*			
someone			cluster			harsh			*contempt*			

Coach: Work from left to right. All five words and/or sounds must be read correctly to earn one tick.				Day								
				Month								

Work from left to right ---------------------------------->

>	con	onfid	confid	onfident	confident							
>	lat	late	gulate	egulate	regulate							
>	andid	candid	didate	andidate	candidate							
>	prost	ostrate	rostrate	prostrate	frustrate							
>	erve	nerve	serve	deserve	conserve							
>	sing	singap	ore	apore	Singapore							
>	mark	arksman	anship	marksman	marksmanship							
>	verm	therm	minate	vermin	terminate							
>	horm	ormon	ormone	hormone	hormonal							
>	inter	rest	terest	interest	interesting							
>	ort	cort	sone	ortisone	cortisone							
>	ulp	sculp	sculpt	ulpture	sculptures							
>	dent	ondent	pondent	respond	respondent							

See unstressed vowels **Page 76**

Coach

This is Your Last Coaching Box!

Ask your student to read the words in the six frames before spelling them.

The frames are: The Wasp frame, The Rich frame, The Do-go frame, The Yes frame, The ire/ore/ure frame, and the any - many frame.

Red letters = names Green letters = sounds

* **Column 3** contains the words: pony - duty - lady etc. The letter 'y' is acting as a vowel and has the same effect as the silent 'e': mate - dine. Your student should read these words then spell them as you would in a normal spelling exercise.

Other Information:

The words 'any' and 'many' in early English had two pronunciations. Broadly speaking: Both words were of German/Dutch origin. The pronunciation would have been 'many and 'any'.   The pronunciation changed to 'menny' and 'enny' but the original spelling remains. In parts of Scotland 'many' and 'any' are the predominant pronunciations.

Day							Day							Day						
Month							Month							Month						
Spell							Spell							Spell						

yes	*do*	any	
this	*does*	many	
bus	*go*	pony	*
plus	*goes*	baby	
gas	*wasp*	lady	
rich	*was*	cosy	
such	*wash*	posy	
much	*want*	duty	
which	*what*	Tony	
ire	*warm*	shady	
ore	*watch*	holy	
ure	*swamp*	Toby	

Read and Pronounce

You have come to the end of the Hornet programme and have gained some understanding of the ability to operate many of the rules of English. **There** are still some rules to grasp but you have proved that you can do it. It's time to address another insect: the **Word** Wasp. You will find the **Word** Wasp as **easy** to use as the Hornet and you will grasp the rules just as quickly. Completing the hard work in the Hornet has given you a head start. The **Word** Wasp offers Hornet students another benefit: You only need one tick from the beginning of the programme to page 93. It is important to start at the beginning in order to make sure that Hornet students have acquired the ability to take on the **Word** Wasp, which has a faster start and a more in depth analysis of the rules and structures of English. We would like to take this opportunity to thank you for **your** hard **work**. We are sure that you will relish using **your** reading and spelling skills.

Good Luck!   Harry and Marie Cowling

Coach: **Underline** and coach incorrect words by demonstrating the appropriate rules and sounds. **A tick must then be gained on a separate day.** Blue = silent Red = names Green = sounds